Rich put an album on the stereo and dropped down beside Kit on the sofa. "So how do you like my parents' mountain cabin?" he asked, winding one of her blond curls around his finger. "It's a great place to unwind after racing cars, especially when I'm here alone with someone like you."

Kit noticed how carefully his hair was styled—you could almost see the tracks his comb had made. The strong scent of his aftershave made her feel slightly sick. Where was Justin? If only he were here beside her. But that was ridiculous; hadn't she lost him forever?

Then, before she knew what was happening, Rich was kissing her. Kit had to fight the impulse to pull away. She told herself she was just nervous. It would get better once she relaxed. Not that she cared what Rich thought—it was Justin she was thinking of . . .

SENIORS™

TOO MUCH TOO SOON
by Eileen Goudge

BANTAM BOOKS
TORONTO • NEW YORK • LONDON • SYDNEY • AUCKLAND

*To Kay, with whom it all began, and to my
mother and father, without whom it
wouldn't have been possible.*

TOO MUCH, TOO SOON
A Bantam Book / September 1986

ISBN 0 553 17257 3

Printed and bound in Great Britain
by Hunt Barnard Printing Ltd.

O   0 9 8 7 6 5 4 3 2 1

Chapter One

"Derek . . . *don't.*"

Kit pushed hard against the hand that was creeping up her T-shirt. Derek had her wedged against the car door, the handle gouging her in the back. His other hand was stubbornly making its way up the seam of her blue jeans.

"Derek, I mean it. If you don't stop I'll . . ." she'd started to say something about screaming, but that seemed too melodramatic somehow. ". . . I'll never speak to you again," she ended weakly.

Her threat didn't even make a dent. Obviously, he wasn't interested in anything she had to say, she thought. Her neck felt damp where he'd been breathing on it. Already, the windshield was fogging up, and it'd only been five minutes since they'd left the library. She felt the hot tickle of tears. How had it gotten out of hand so fast? It

1

had started out to be fun—the flirting part, at least. Kit enjoyed flirting. She found it hard to resist a boy when he got that sleepy, unfocused look in his eyes. That I-want-to-kiss-you look. Her biggest trouble, she reflected, was that she never stopped to think whether or not it was what *she* wanted until it was too late.

But was it all *her* fault? Did boys treat all girls this way? Since when did a few kisses become a passport to go all the way?

Kit stiffened in panic as Derek reached up and began fumbling with her bra strap. "I'm not kidding. I'm serious, really serious. I want you to cut it out this second!"

"Hey," he said soothingly in a strange thick voice. He didn't sound at all like the Derek who had helped her work out a trig problem only half an hour ago. "What're you getting so worked up about?"

"I'm not the one who's worked up," she answered, fighting to keep the tears out of her voice.

"I'm not hurting you, am I? Relax."

"I can't relax. There's something stabbing me in the back, and I can't breathe with you on top of me."

"Why didn't you say so in the first place? Look, I'll fold the back seat down. That way we can stretch out and get comfortable."

"That's not what I meant," she said. "Derek, I just want to go home. *Please.* I'm meeting my friends in a little while and I don't want to be late."

2

"They'll understand." He went back to nibbling on her neck. "What're friends for?"

Suddenly, Kit had had all she could take. Anchoring both palms against his chest, she heaved with all her strength. Derek jerked backwards, cracking his shaggy blond head against the rearview mirror.

"Hey!" He glared at her, his blue eyes dark with anger, as he rubbed the back of his head. "What did you do that for?"

"You were acting like a jerk, that's why," she said, refusing to look at him. Her eyes brimmed with tears. She used to think Derek was handsome, but not anymore. Now she noticed that his chin sloped into his neck a little too far and that his eyes were on the beady side. He also had an annoying habit of flicking his hair off his forehead every few seconds.

Derek glared at her another minute or so, then finally, he turned away with a shrug. "I can't figure you out. Boy, I must be really dense or something. I thought you wanted me to . . ."

"I did," Kit said softly. She was starting to feel a little guilty about the way she'd acted. "The kissing part. After that . . . well, I just didn't feel like it."

"But I thought . . . I mean, I heard . . ." Derek wore an embarrassed look. Then, he said gruffly, "Hey, look, let's just call it an evening, okay? I'll take you home." He started the engine abruptly. It caught with a shriek of protest.

Kit straightened, wiping a hole in the

3

steamed-up windshield so she could see out. The front steps of the library retreated from view, then they were turning onto Glenwood Drive, heading past the sprawling buildings and the carefully tended lawn of Glenwood High. Some-one had forgotten to lower the flag, she noticed. It slapped in the breeze, looking as if it were salut-ing the full moon that was rising overhead.

They continued driving through the main part of Glenwood, which consisted of two stoplights linked together by a street of artsy-looking shops, a gas station, and a small shopping center. Huge spreading oaks, left uncut when the town was built a hundred years or so ago, seemed to crouch over the buildings like overprotective parents. It was Friday, so the pub on the corner of Farm Hill looked busy, but otherwise Glenwood was the kind of place that most nights put the lights out and pulled the covers up by eight o'clock.

Kit bit her lip to keep from crying. Derek didn't need to tell her what he'd "heard." She knew all too well what her reputation was at school. She had no idea what people said exactly, but the looks were enough. She hated it when she had to pass a bunch of boys and they gave her the Look. Conversation would stop and their eyes would follow her to her locker, watching while she fum-bled with the combination. It was worse at the drinking fountain, where she would have to bend her knees and sort of scrunch down so as not to make a spectacle of herself. But it was the Daisy Mae poster that said it best of all.

Last semester, Kit had been picked to play Daisy Mae in the school production of *Li'l Abner*. When the poster came out, sketched by a boy in her art class who was always giving her the Look, Kit could hardly believe her eyes. It was an exact likeness of her, as far as caricatures go. There was the tousled blond hair looking as if she'd just tumbled out of bed, big, sleepy blue eyes spiked with long dark lashes, and full sensuous mouth—all exaggerated to extremes. Then there was the Body. You could see Daisy Mae's saucy little bottom winking out at you from the back of her tattered cutoffs. Enormous breasts spilled over the top of her skimpy blouse. The worst part was, that despite the exaggeration, it looked just like her. Kit had felt herself blush every time she was faced with that poster.

There was something else she'd discovered about being seventeen and having a Body that made boys Look. Looks were always followed by Talk. It didn't matter if it was true or not, the talk was the same regardless.

Derek pulled up in front of the apartment building where she lived. He didn't bother to get out and walk her to the door. He left the motor running while she jumped out.

"I'll call you," he said in a tight voice. Kit hated it when boys lied like that, but she didn't care if he called her or not. She hoped he wouldn't.

Kit cut across the overgrown lawn without looking back. Inside, a narrow staircase led to the third floor. In the corridor she was immediately

5

assaulted by leftover dinner smells, the muffled sounds of TV sets, and squabbling voices. She could never walk down this bleak hallway without thinking about the house on Redwood Street. If she closed her eyes, she could picture it more clearly than where she was: her attic room with the sloping walls she'd covered in pretty flowered wallpaper, the window facing out on the gold-green hills of Palo Alto. Thinking about it made her stomach curl up in a tight fist.

What she missed most these days was her father. How she wished she could see him more often. What she liked remembering best were the times before the divorce—when they were a family. Back in those days, her Daddy used to crack dumb little jokes at the dinner table, and her Mom would sit on his lap sometimes.

Last year, her father's company had transferred him to Los Angeles. A few months before that, he'd gotten married again—to a small, plumpish woman named Vi, short for Violet, who had two daughters younger than Kit. Vi wasn't a bit like Mom. For one thing, she loved to cook. She also had this incredible thing about vacuuming. Kit had noticed that if a crumb or a piece of lint appeared on the carpet, Vi would whip out her vacuum cleaner like a general going into battle. Mom's attitude about housework was just the opposite. She once told Kit she didn't want it inscribed on her tombstone that she'd had the cleanest oven in town. So even though Vi went out of her way to be nice, Kit couldn't help feeling nervous around her. Kit and Mom were so much alike; if Daddy preferred Vi's kind of woman, where did that leave her?

Kit looked for her mother as she entered her apartment, finding her finally in the bathroom; she was applying Ultra-Lash to her ultra-long eyelashes. Janice McCoy didn't look like anyone's mother, Kit had decided long ago, and she had mixed feelings about that. Part of Kit felt proud when people told her what a knockout her mother was, or when they were mistaken for sisters. But part of Kit still cherished the childish wish that Janice were, well, a little more on the apron-wearing side. Still, she couldn't really imagine Janice in an apron. Neither could Janice, which had been a contributing factor in the divorce. Whenever she cooked, she simply tied a dish towel around her slender waist. Right now, though, she was wearing her forest-green cocktail dress and Grandma Hennessey's pearls. She looked breathtaking.

"I hope he appreciates it," Kit said.

"Who?" Janice asked, greeting her daughter with a distracted smile.

"Whoever you're going out with. Shall I guess?" She picked up a hairbrush, pretending it was a microphone. "Who will it be tonight, folks? Will the lucky winner of the Janice McCoy sweepstakes please step forward? Let's give him a big hand, folks!"

Janice erupted in laughter. "Now look what you made me do. I've got mascara all over my eyelid." She dabbed at it with a Kleenex.

"I don't know, Mom. I think it looks cute. You could always tell him you got a black eye while defending your honor."

"Cute, Kit, very cute."

"Don't blame me for my lousy sense of humor. I inherited it from you, remember?"

"I'll try to keep that in mind." Kit was alerted by the sound of the intercom buzzing in the next room. "Honey, would you get that? It's probably Doug."

"Doug who?" Kit asked, feeling her kidding mood evaporate.

"Doug Martin. You remember, you met him last week when he took me to the company banquet. He works upstairs in Personnel. No, wait, that was the night you were over at Lori's. Well, don't worry, he's very nice. You'll like him."

"What happened to Peter?" Kit wanted to know. "Aren't you going out with him anymore?"

Janice was fiddling with her pearls now, trying to arrange them so they wouldn't get lost in her cleavage. She wasn't having much luck.

"Of course I'm still seeing Peter. Peter and I are friends. That doesn't mean I don't have the right to see other people, too." She looked at Kit. "Hey, wait a minute. Why do I get the feeling I have to justify all this to you? Who's the mother here, anyway?"

It was an old joke with them, but this time Kit didn't even crack a smile. "I'll get the door," she said.

8

"Besides," Janice called cheerfully after her, "I don't see you sitting home much these days. What's good for the goose, is good for the goose's mother!"

God, her mother could be so corny sometimes, Kit thought. Out of Janice's sight, she gave in to a tiny smile. They made a good team. A couple of real coconuts, Dad used to say. She just wished . . . oh, how she wished sometimes that Janice would act more like a mother than a big sister.

How could she explain to Janice about Derek, for instance? "Sex is as natural as breathing," Mom always said. Of course, she didn't mean people should go around doing it whenever they felt like it—just that when the right person came along, at the right time, everything should come naturally after that.

But for Kit, the idea of having sex never seemed natural. At first, she would be swept away by the kissing. That made her feel warm and tingly, but those good feelings never lasted very long. Little by little, awareness would start creeping in. She would begin to notice that the boy was making funny noises in his throat, and breathing a little too hard. Panic would start setting in about the time he began fumbling with her zipper or (heaven forbid) his own. It was then that Kit would have an overwhelming urge to do one thing: escape! Sex might be natural, she thought, but so were earthquakes and hurricanes.

Once, Kit tried to tell her mother how she felt,

and Janice told her not to worry. Kit was still so young, her mother said, she'd feel differently when she was older. But Kit wasn't sure. She thought of the nights she'd lain awake listening, or rather, trying *not* to listen, to the noises drifting through the wall that separated Mom's bedroom from her own. Nothing could shut them out, not even the pillow she squashed around her head like some kind of ridiculous crash helmet. But that was how sex made her feel—like she was hurtling down some mysterious road toward certain disaster.

Not that men slept over every night, Kit was quick to remind herself. Janice had had three or four boyfriends since the divorce, but she was young and gorgeous, so it was only to be expected, right?

Kit pressed down on the "talk" button. "Who is it?"

She wasn't too surprised when a man's voice answered, "Janice?" People often confused their voices.

"No. This is her daughter."

"Oh. You sound just alike."

Kit pressed the button to let him in. Then she went into her room to pack an overnight bag. She was sleeping over at Elaine's tonight. They all were—Alex and Lori, too—her best friends. The prospect of seeing them lifted her spirits. What would she do without her friends?

Sometimes, she felt closer to them than anyone else on earth. They could tell each other everything. They could laugh and cry together, yell and scream at each other if they felt like it, and somehow it all came out right. Tonight, they were getting together to practice the barbershop quartet they were doing for the Senior Vaudeville in a couple of weeks. Maybe they could get through it just this once without dissolving into giggles.

"Kit?" Her mother knocked lightly on the door. "Doug's here. Why don't you come out and meet him?"

"Some other time, Mom. I'm in the middle of getting dressed." It was a lie, but she saw no reason for spoiling her mother's good time by telling the truth.

Janice didn't argue. For a few seconds there was the low murmur of voices, then the front door clicked shut. Kit sank down on the bed. Her room was as cramped as the rest of the apartment, with barely enough space for her bed, a small pine dresser, and a few bookshelves. A Degas ballet print hung on one wall. The other wall was covered with the oriental fans she collected.

Kit sat facing the window, which offered a glorious moonlit view of the fire escape and Mrs. Lanitsky's clothesline across the way. She stared out at a pair of pajama bottoms flapping forlornly in the breeze, then for no reason at all, suddenly burst into tears.

Chapter Two

"Quick! I need your help!"

Kit was taken by surprise as Elaine grabbed her elbow, steering her off the back porch into the kitchen. Kit followed her friend over to the stove, and peered skeptically into the pot that was bubbling on the stove.

"It's supposed to be fudge," Elaine groaned. "But it looks more like molten lava. Do you think it's hopeless?" When she looked up, Kit couldn't resist a smile at the way Elaine's big glasses were steamed over.

"I don't know," Kit said. "In a pinch we could always use it to patch a leaky roof." She hugged her friend. "Don't worry, Elaine, we don't expect you to be a great cook. Isn't being smart enough? I'll bet Einstein couldn't boil water."

"Einstein didn't have three starving friends to feed."

"Speaking of friends—where are Alex and Lori? Shouldn't they be here by now?"

Elaine stuck her head around the corner to glance at the grandfather clock that was wedged in the corner beside a tall chrome-and-glass bookcase. Elaine's whole house was a hodge-podge of old and new, a mixture that Kit found irresistible. Elaine often joked about it saying her parents had "fancy" tastes—they bought whatever struck their fancy, whether or not it fit in with the rest of their furniture. The result was a crazy quilt of a house crammed full of people, plants, cats and dogs.

To Kit, it seemed as though Elaine stood in the middle of it all like the tranquil eye of a hurricane. She was calm and serious, and had the wonderful ability to shut out the rest of the world when she was absorbed in something. She could sit for hours, perfectly at peace, with her nose buried in a book, while the TV roared, the doorbell jangled, and siblings and animals tumbled around her. When it came to studying, she had a mind like Vi's vacuum cleaner. She could zip through a homework assignment faster than anyone.

Elaine didn't even look like the rest of the family. Her parents and three sisters were all on the stubby side, with blond hair and blue eyes. Elaine was tall and slender, with dark hair that fell straight to her shoulders. Oversized glasses framed a pair of eyes the color of nutmeg, tipped slightly up at the corners to give her an oddly exotic look that clashed with the conservative way she dressed. Kit was always telling her how fantastic her eyes would look with a little eye-shadow and mascara, but Elaine claimed makeup wasn't her style. *Her* style, as she put it, was more on the Preppie-Plaid side—or Preppie-*Drab*, as her friends sometimes teased. Kit saw nothing wrong with the way Elaine looked, though. In fact, she thought Elaine was quite pretty in spite of her attempts to play down her appearance.

Elaine always kidded Kit that she was jealous of her eye-catching looks, but the truth was, Kit felt she had more reason to be envious of Elaine. There was the warm family atmosphere of her home, for one thing. And then there was Elaine's smartness. Elaine seemed to know where she was going. She was . . . well, centered. If Kit had to compare, her own center would resemble that of a jelly doughnut.

"Alex called to say she was picking up Lori," Elaine explained. "But that was twenty minutes ago."

"Knowing Alex, she would probably make it faster on foot. I wonder what's keeping them." Kit dipped a spoon in the fudge, blowing on it before she tasted it. "Mmm. Not bad for molten lava."

"Speaking of molten," Elaine said, lowering her voice, "how did it go with Derek?"

Kit blushed. Elaine always seemed to be able to read her mind. Though she loved all her friends, she felt closer to Elaine than the others. For one thing, she'd known Elaine longer—since the

14

third grade. She would never forget the day skinny bespectacled Elaine Gregory arrived at school with a sanitary napkin wrapped around one scraped knee. Kit took one look and quickly steered her into the girl's bathroom. She'd never spoken to Elaine before this; she was the smartest person in class, and Kit had always been a little in awe of her.

"You can't go in like that," Kit had said.

Elaine blinked in confusion. "Why not?"

Kit told her. Elaine turned bright red. "My mother wasn't home. I—I thought they were bandages," she stammered.

"Don't worry, anyone could've made the same mistake," Kit reassured her generously.

She didn't believe it for one minute, but she didn't want Elaine to feel bad. Also, deep down inside, she was glad to know Elaine the Brain wasn't so smart about everything after all. It evened things out, somehow.

In that moment, their friendship was forged—a bond that had survived their many differences and grown deeper with each passing year.

"Kit?" Elaine's concerned voice jolted her back to the present. "I was just kidding, okay? I know it was just a study date."

Kit looked around to see if anyone was listening, but judging from the war whoops coming from the den, the whole family was engaged in their nightly Scrabble game.

"Some study date! All he wanted to study was

my anatomy." Kit's eyes filled with tears.

"Did he—" Elaine bit her lip, unable to continue. The subject of boys usually caused her to grow tongue-tied.

Kit shook her head, brushing angrily at her tears. "It's so stupid. I don't even know why I'm crying. It's nothing that hasn't happened before. I should be used to it by now."

With a deep sigh, Elaine gathered her friend in her arms. Kit gave a miserable sniff into her shoulder.

"Look, I'm probably the worst person in the world to advise you on this," Elaine said. "I mean, what do I know? When it comes to boys, I'm no Einstein. More like Casper the Friendly Ghost." She drew back, poking her glasses into place. "But it seems if you want boys to notice you less, maybe you shouldn't, uh, well, *advertise* so much."

Kit was crushed. Her cheeks flaming, she echoed, "Advertise? What do you mean?"

"Oh, Kit . . . *I* know what you're like, but the way you dress, some people might get the wrong impression. Namely, any boy with twenty-twenty vision."

"What's wrong with the way I'm dressed?" Kit wanted to know.

She positioned herself in front of the mirrored armoire by the refrigerator. A funny thing to have in the kitchen, she'd always thought, but Mrs. Gregory used it to store her extra dishes and canned stuff. Kit gazed at her reflection in dismay, seeing herself for the first time through Elaine's eyes. She fingered the bow on her skimpy camisole top, suddenly feeling self-conscious.

"Nothing's wrong with it," Elaine said. "That is, if you don't mind creating a stampede wherever you go. Look, Kit, I'm not criticizing you. You're my best friend—I *love* you. If I looked like you, I'm not so sure I'd want to cover it up, either." She put her arm around Kit. "I'm just trying to help."

"I know," Kit answered, still feeling miserable. She picked a dry leaf from the philodendron that trailed over the sink. The trouble is, I want boys to notice me. I just don't know how to handle it when they do. Am I crazy or what?"

"You're not crazy. With me, it's just the opposite—I hide from boys, but at the same time I'm hoping they'll notice me somehow." She sighed deeply. "Sometimes I think being seventeen is another word for temporary insanity."

Knowing that Elaine was just as confused as she was suddenly made Kit feel better. Maybe there was hope for her yet. She straightened her shoulders, managing a small smile. She wouldn't allow herself to stay depressed.

Kit turned to Elaine. "You make awful fudge, but you give good advice."

"The fudge!" Elaine rushed back to the stove just as a froth of brown bubbles spilled over the top of the pan. She snatched it off the burner. Just then the phone rang.

"I'll get it," Kit said and picked up the receiver.

"Someone in Detroit doesn't like me," a girl's voice declared. "This is the third time in one week this darn wreck has cut out on me!"

Kit laughed. "Hi, Alex," she said. "Tell me where you are and we'll pick you up."

"Count me out," Elaine called over her shoulder as she stirred the fudge. "I think Mount Vesuvius is about to boil over again."

Ten minutes later, Kit was pulling to a stop beside a battered green Dodge Dart parked off Glenwood Drive. Alex was nowhere in sight. Then Kit spotted a pair of tanned muscular legs sticking out from underneath the back end. They were soon followed by a T-shirt clad chest and a head capped by sleek mahogany-colored hair. Kit wasn't a bit surprised to see her friend this way—Alex, to say the least, was hardly the conventional type. While her hobby wasn't fixing cars or anything, she did know a little about them and saw no reason for getting someone else to do a job she was perfectly capable of doing herself.

A lot of it had to do with the kind of family she came from. Alex Enomoto's parents were both superachievers. Her father was a doctor—a dermatologist, actually—whom Alex often jokingly called Dr. Zit. Although he was born in Japan, his parents, Alex's grandparents, emigrated to the United States when he was about ten, so he grew up attending American public schools and universities. He was also a talented musician. In

18

fact, he played the piano so well that the local symphony would invite him, on occasion, to perform with it, which he did as a hobby. Alex's mother, an excellent artist, had her own graphics design business. She had been a professional singer in the past, but now, she too just sang for fun.

She and Dr. Enomoto had met each other when they were performing in a benefit concert—she was singing the aria from *Madame Butterfly*; he was playing the *Moonlight Sonata*. They were married three weeks later. It was the most romantic thing Kit had ever heard, and she always sighed wistfully when Alex told the story. Her own parents had met over a loaf of pumpernickel bread in the supermarket. Maybe that was why their marriage hadn't lasted. What kind of basis was pumpernickel bread for a lasting relationship?

Alex flashed Kit a warm smile. "Hand me the sprocket wrench," she said. "It's in the tool box under the seat."

Kit unearthed the wrench and passed it down to Alex. "You spend more time fixing it than you do riding in it. Why don't you get another car?"

Alex's smile widened into a grin. "I like challenges."

Alex had just described herself in a nutshell, Kit thought. She was like the mountain climber who, when asked why he'd climbed Mount Everest, replied, "Because it was there." Alex didn't need a reason to perform surgery on a clunky old car twice a week, or to swim a hundred laps a day. She did it just because.

It was one of the reasons Kit loved her. And just like everything else she tackled, Alex would no more quit on a friendship than she would drop out of a race before the finish line.

Alex tinkered with the engine for a few more minutes until she realized it was hopeless; she was missing a crucial replacement part.

"Let's go," she said, brushing off the back of her shorts. "Lori's probably chewing her nails by now. I told her I'd pick her up half an hour ago."

On their way over to Lori's, Kit recounted the fiasco with Derek.

"I still don't know why I got so upset," she confessed. "I mean, he was pushy, but I can't really blame him. I guess I sort of led him on." She was thinking about what Elaine had told her.

"Don't worry about Derek," Alex said. "He'll survive."

"I'm not worried about Derek. But what happens if . . . well, next time it's a guy I really like? Suppose he kisses me and I freak out and ruin everything?"

"Got someone in mind?" Alex asked with her usual knack for cutting right to the heart of the matter.

Kit could feel the heat rush to her cheeks. In her mind she pictured a tall sandy-haired boy with quiet gray eyes. She hadn't told her friends about Justin Kennerly yet. He was a boy she worked with at Gennaro's Pizza. He also went to Glenwood High, but they didn't share any classes. Anyway, what was there to tell, she thought. Nothing had happened so far. The way it was going, probably nothing ever would. Even though they saw each other at the pizza parlor three days a week, Justin never acted more than casually friendly toward her. She'd tried flirting with him, but that had gotten her nowhere. Did he have a girlfriend? she wondered. She wished she could stop thinking about him. In the past two weeks alone, she'd burned three batches of onion rings daydreaming about Justin.

"What makes you think I have someone in mind?" she asked.

"You," Alex said. "You have that look in your eye."

Kit shifted uncomfortably. Suddenly, the car seemed too warm, even though she had all the windows rolled down. Was it so obvious? Had Justin noticed, too?

Kit sighed. "Okay, but that's as far as it's going to go," she said, turning her VW bug into Lori's driveway. "I'll probably stay a virgin for the rest of my life."

"There are worse things," Alex pointed out. "Sex isn't everything, you know. I've always wondered why they make such a big deal out of it. From what I've seen it looks like more buildup than action. Like running the mile race. You spend half your life getting ready for it, and five minutes actually doing it."

"You're probably right. But I can't help the way it *seems*. I guess that's the difference between thinking about something and actually *doing* it."

Alex laid a hand on her arm. "Seriously, Kit, you shouldn't be so hard on yourself. With Danny, I sometimes feel the same way. We'll be kissing and everything's going great, then all of a sudden I feel this *pressure* to, you know, take that next step and I sort of want to, only I realize I'd be doing it mostly for Danny." Her large brown eyes flashed under the terry sweatband she wore. "Don't you see? It has to be for *me* as much as for him."

Many times, Kit had watched Alex and Danny—both were on the swim team together—doing laps in the pool after school. They moved together so gracefully, their bodies seemed to fall into a natural synchrony. Obviously, their thoughts blended in the same way. Kit envied them. Would she ever find a boy who was special like that? Someone who could understand not only how mixed-up her feelings got, but also that her mind and her body didn't always see eye to eye?

Kit beeped her horn for Lori.

"Don't push yourself," Alex repeated. "There's plenty of time."

"I won't," Kit promised. "I'm not in any hurry."

But that wasn't strictly true, was it? Sometimes, she couldn't wait to grow up, to be a woman, a real woman who didn't run away when a boy kissed her.

Then again, sometimes she felt she could gladly stay seventeen forever.

Chapter Three

"I hate sad endings," Lori sniffed.

Kit handed her the box of Kleenex that was on the coffee table. They were watching the late movie on TV while Elaine and Alex scrounged in the kitchen for something to eat. They'd polished off the fudge hours ago.

"It's more like real life this way," Kit pointed out. "In real life, things hardly ever turn out completely happy. Well, maybe for a while they do, but sooner or later it all gets confused again."

"Who wants movies to be like real life?"

Lori was looking at Kit with wide blue eyes, her eyelashes spiky with tears. Lori had the most perfect face Kit had ever seen—except in magazines. But even the models in magazines probably didn't look that good in real life. Lori really did. She had an exquisitely sculpted face with fine, high cheekbones and enormous blue eyes fringed with long dark lashes. Lori's lashes were so long they nearly touched her eyebrows. She told Kit that when she was younger she got teased so much she once cut them off. Kit found it hard to believe that anyone as beautiful as Lori wouldn't automatically *know* she was beautiful, but Lori honestly didn't. Whenever someone gave her a compliment and she said, "You think so?" she was really asking, not just pretending to be modest the way some girls did.

Lori was also the most sensitive one in the group, Kit thought. She cried at everything. Sad movies. Or if she read in the paper about a plane crash where fifty people got killed. She even got choked up if anyone else cried in front of her—even if she didn't know what they were crying about.

At school, Lori's sensitivity took the form of terrible shyness, which some people mistakenly took for snobbishness. It was too bad they didn't try harder to get to know her, because Lori was so *nice* and was such a loyal friend. No favor was ever too much to ask, as far as she was concerned. Kit felt as if she'd known Lori forever, even though she was the newcomer of their group; Lori and her mother had only moved to Glenwood last year.

"You're right," Kit agreed with a laugh. "Happy endings may not make much sense, but they're more fun. Can you imagine our lives as a TV show?"

"In my case, there isn't much to show," Lori

said with a soft giggle. It was her trademark, that giggle. "It would be pretty boring."

"We could always spice it up. We could say you were a . . . let me see, a princess in your former life. You got kicked out of your castle when the Huns took over, and you escaped to Glenwood."

Lori laughed. She tossed her satiny blond hair over one shoulder. "I didn't know there were any Huns left."

"There probably aren't. It just sounded good. What's the point of having a secret past that's boring?"

Lori's expression grew thoughtful. Sometimes Kit got the feeling there was something Lori wasn't telling them. Something that was on her mind a lot. But that was crazy, wasn't it? True, she didn't talk much about her life before she moved to Glenwood, but what was there to talk about? She probably went to school and did the same boring stuff as everyone else. All Kit knew was that Lori's father had died not too long ago. Lori didn't like talking about it. Who could blame her? For anyone as sensitive as Lori, it was probably a tremendous blow.

Kit could easily relate to Lori's reluctance to talk about the past. She could never talk about life in the old days—before her parents got divorced. Those feelings were too private to share even with her best friends.

Maybe it was just coincidence that Lori was so quick to change the subject. "Do you think we should practice the routine some more?" she asked.

Earlier, it had seemed to Kit that they were starting to sound pretty good—until Alex began clowning around and Lori got to laughing so hard she could hardly stand up.

"Not me. I'm beat," Alex called out, sailing in with a platter of sandwiches. Elaine tagged after with an ice-cream carton in one hand and four spoons in the other.

Elaine collapsed onto the couch with an incredulous expression. "You? You never get tired. You could probably run the fifty-yard dash in your sleep."

"Only the fifty-yard?" joked Alex. She settled cross-legged on the carpet, pulling the Gregorys' cat, a large ginger tom, into her lap.

"Poor Bessie," Kit said, leaning over to stroke his twitching tail. "I think it's mean to call a tomcat Bessie. You should've thought up a new name after you figured out he was a boy. I mean, how embarrassing!"

"He's a cat," Elaine replied with her usual matter-of-factness. "Cats don't get embarrassed."

"Think how it would be if people never got embarrassed," Lori remarked. "We'd probably all walk around naked."

"What a horrible thought!" Kit gasped. Instinctively, she snatched up a throw pillow, hugging it to her chest.

"I didn't say we *should*," Lori quickly defended herself. "Personally, I'd rather *die* first."

"I don't see what's so bad about it," Alex said. Her eyes held a devilish glint. "Think how much more honest it would be. For instance, if you liked a boy, you could tell right away whether or not he liked you back."

Kit nearly choked on her sandwich. "God, Alex, you're *awful*. How can you joke about a thing like *that*?"

"It's easier if you joke about it once in a while." Alex went back to stroking Bessie. His purring filled the room. "People take sex far too seriously, don't you think? It's supposed to be fun, right?"

"Hand-to-hand combat isn't exactly my idea of fun," Kit said.

"That's the whole point. If we didn't make such a big deal about it, maybe we could relax and enjoy it more."

"I think," Elaine said, "that it would depend on how you felt about the person. If you really cared about each other, it'd be different."

"You mean you'd have to be in love?" Lori asked her.

"Not necessarily. It would help, but probably what's most important is for the two people involved to really like each other. Friendship should count more than sex appeal." Elaine gave a wistful sigh and dug her spoon into the ice cream. "Of course, I wouldn't mind settling for a little more in the sex appeal department, myself."

"I've never been in love," Lori recalled, "but when I was twelve, I had this tremendous crush on my orthodontist. Whenever he got up real

27

close and stared into my mouth, I couldn't breathe. It got so bad there were these couple of times when I thought I was going to pass out. Finally, I decided being that crazy about someone wasn't worth all the misery it caused."

Kit got up and went over to the window. She liked looking out at Elaine's backyard, which was a jumble of flowers, with a vegetable garden mixed in somewhere. A rusting jungle gym sprouted up out of the midst of it, which Elaine referred to as the family's historical monument.

"I wish making love could be like . . . dancing," Kit said quietly. She lifted her arms and executed a perfect pirouette.

There was nothing unnatural about dancing, she decided. No awkward bumping of limbs. No mumbled excuses. Just pure, graceful movement. When she really got into it, she didn't even have to think about her body. She was part of the air, the music. Kit's dream was to be a professional dancer someday. The only reason (besides Justin, of course) she was working at Gennaro's was to earn enough money to pay for her dance lessons. Kit had no choice; there was no way Janice could afford it on her salary.

Kit looked around as Mrs. Gregory appeared at the doorway, hugging a frilly bathrobe to her plump chest.

"I hate to break this up, girls, but it's getting awfully late. *You* may not need your beauty sleep, but I need all I can get."

"In a minute, Mom," Elaine said, a smile playing at her lips. "Kit was just explaining the finer points of dance to us."

Kit shot Elaine a murderous look, but Mrs. Gregory only smiled. "I'll bet," she said.

"Come on," Elaine said when her mother had gone back upstairs. "We can talk more after we get into our sleeping bags."

"Yeah, it's easier to talk about the juicy stuff with the lights out," Alex said.

Kit sighed. "I remember when all we ever told at slumber parties were ghost stories."

"Ghost stories, and hot chocolate after when we were too scared to go to sleep," Elaine recalled with a laugh. She pushed the coffee table against the bookcase to make room for their sleeping bags.

A wave of bittersweet nostalgia swept over Kit. "What happened to us?"

"We grew up, that's what," Alex said, adding with a grimace, "At least, I *hope* we did."

Kit felt a shudder of uneasiness pass through her. Right now, she would have settled for a good scary ghost story chased by a mug of lumpy hot chocolate. Being grown-up, she decided, wasn't all it was cracked up to be.

Chapter Four

The first thing Kit noticed when she stepped off the bus on Monday was Justin's rust-red Toyota parked out in front of Gennaro's Pizza. Her heart beat faster as she crossed the street. Going in, she caught her reflection in the big glass door and stopped to straighten her skirt—a bright red mini with a matching polka dot top. She suddenly felt very conscious of how she looked. Not that it made any difference, she was quick to remind herself. As far as Justin was concerned, she might as well be invisible.

Mr. Watkins looked up with a frown as she walked in. Her boss was a small, wiry man with reddish hair parted on the side and combed over his bald spot. When Kit was little, she'd pictured a pizza parlor as a place where a fat, smiling man with rolled-up sleeves spun pizza dough in the air and spoke in broken English to his customers.

Mr. Watkins wasn't fat or smiling (or even Italian, as far as she knew) and the only time he rolled up his sleeves was when he took inventory, which was what he was doing at the moment.

"You're late," he said, tapping his pen impatiently against his clipboard. "The third time this month."

"I'm sorry, Mr. Watkins. Really I am," Kit said, her words rushing out. "My last class ran late, then I missed my bus and had to wait for the n—"

He waved aside her excuses. "Just see that it doesn't happen again. I've been very patient with you, young lady. If you could see the stack of applications on my desk from kids who would give anything to have your job . . ." he left the threat hanging, as he always did.

So far, Kit had seen no evidence of this tremendous competition, but she decided it was best to stay on the safe side. This job, even with all its drawbacks, was too important to her. She simply couldn't afford to lose it.

Kit swallowed hard. "It won't happen again, Mr. Watkins. I promise."

He grunted in reply and went back to examining the sheet of figures on his clipboard. Kit figured he'd been lying in wait for her, ready to pounce; otherwise, he would have been in his office instead of sitting out here in one of the booths. Mondays she skipped study hall to get here early, so actually Mr. Watkins had nothing to complain about. Try telling him that, though, she thought.

31

Actually, she wouldn't have minded working someplace else. Gennaro's, aside from Justin, was a pretty depressing place. Mr. Watkins's idea of jazzing it up had been to stick a couple of fake plants in the window and paint the walls orange. The orange clashed horribly with the red leatherette booths, which the sun had faded to an unhealthy pink. Even the pizza wasn't very good. The only reason for the restaurant's success, Kit had long ago decided, was its short distance from Glenwood High and the fact that the food in the school cafeteria was even worse. Plus, it was the only pizza parlor in town.

Anyway, there was no point in fantasizing. This position was the best she was going to get. Jobs were hard to find in a town the size of Glenwood. Maybe it was a little easier in Palo Alto, but that was six miles away. With all the running back and forth she would have to do, there wouldn't be any time left for her dance lessons.

Kit ducked into the kitchen before Mr. Watkins could change his mind about firing her. The kitchen, with its comfortable clutter and warm steamy smells, was a welcome change from the garish exterior. She found a clean apron on the hook by the door and tied it around her.

"Hi!" Justin greeted her without looking up. He was busy rolling out a glob of dough, his forearms dusty with flour.

Kit's pulse kicked into high gear. Why did he have to be so good-looking? Why couldn't he be short and fat, or scrawny and pimpled? Instead, here she was, stuck with someone who made her feel as if she were coming down with a fever every time she looked at him.

Not that Justin was so incredibly handsome, she thought. He probably wasn't handsome at all—at least, not in the conventional sense. He was tall, more rangy than muscular, with the kind of face she could have stared at for hours. It was such an interesting face, long and craggy— yet sensitive. His cheekbones formed narrow, crescent-shaped ridges above a nose that had a slight adorable bump in the middle, and his jawline was sharply defined. Then there were his eyes. They were the calm gray of an early morning sky, the time of day Kit liked best. Every time she looked into Justin's eyes, she felt certain that good thoughts lay behind them.

"Hi there, yourself!" she chirped, fluttering her eyelashes at him when he finally glanced up. Kit the Flirt. It was a role she adopted the way some girls put on makeup. She was afraid that if Justin knew how nervous and insecure she really was, he would like her even less than he already did.

"What's wrong with Mr. Watkins?" she asked. "He was really in a bad mood when I came in. Worse than usual, that is."

Justin shrugged, reaching up to brush a sandy curl from his forehead with the back of his bony wrist. "Search me."

"I probably should," Kit teased, flicking him with the end of her dishtowel as she pranced past. "You quiet types are the ones to watch out for. I mean, you could be an international terrorist for all I know. Maybe you've got a gun under your apron, and you're planning to hold us all hostage until your demands are met."

Justin smiled and went back to mashing his dough with a rolling pin. After a little while, he said, "Would you mind getting some cheese from the freezer? We're getting a little low."

Kit fought the urge to hit him—this time with something harder than her towel. Why did he ignore her when she was trying so hard to get his attention? At school, it was a different matter; she hardly ever saw him anyway, since they didn't have any classes together. But here, where there wasn't anyone else to talk to, Kit thought she would have rated slightly better than a lump of pizza dough. Apparently she was wrong.

The front door buzzer sounded, alerting Kit that customers were arriving. She was glad this was her week to stand behind the counter and take orders. Feeling miserable, she slipped out of the kitchen, keeping her head high and her expression as neutral as possible. She wouldn't give Justin the satisfaction of seeing that he could hurt her.

First, a couple came up to the register who spent ten minutes arguing about what they didn't want on their pizza. The husband hated mushrooms, the wife said pepperoni gave her gas. Finally, they settled on two small pizzas instead of one large one. When Kit rang up their order, she handed them each a happy-face pizza button—Mr. Watkins' latest campaign in good-will advertising.

During the next hour, she handed out pizzas and pitchers of root beer for a party of six-year-olds celebrating a birthday, and waited on a dozen more people who couldn't make up their minds. Kit couldn't have been more relieved when, around four-thirty, Elaine and Lori breezed in through the door.

"Give me a double sausage, hold the pizza," joked Lori. She patted her stomach. "I'm on a diet." Kit thought she looked spectacular in a lavender jumpsuit striped with pale pink, not an extra pound in sight.

"You're *always* on a diet," Elaine said teasingly. She took off her glasses, which were steamed up from their bike ride over, and wiped them on a paper napkin plucked from the stainless-steel holder by the register. "One of these days, you're going to get so skinny, we'll have to tie a string around you to keep you from blowing away."

"Where's Alex?" Kit wanted to know.

"She's in training for a meet, remember?" Elaine reminded her. "No junk food for a whole week. Sounds like cruel and inhuman punishment to me. She ought to complain to the Human Rights Commission."

Kit laughed. "Junk food? If Mr. Watkins had his way, he'd make pizza the main staple of the American diet."

"I thought it already was," Elaine said, straight-faced.

"Speaking of the devil," Lori said, lowering her voice, "Where's your boss?"

"He's probably in back giving someone twenty lashes for not finishing their pizza," Elaine giggled.

"It's no joke," Kit said. "You should've seen the way he acted when I came in late today. He practically snapped my head off!"

Lori winced. "I don't know how you can stand it. Is he that mean to Justin?"

"Sure." Kit ducked down below the counter, pretending to be looking for something. She didn't want her friends to see the blush that had crept into her cheeks as soon as Justin's name was mentioned. "I'll say one thing about Mr. Watkins—he doesn't discriminate. I've seen him chew Justin out for the dumbest little things. The difference is, it doesn't seem to bother Justin. *Nothing* gets to him."

She popped up to find Elaine staring at her with one of her famous are-you-telling-all-there-is expressions. Her eyebrows were arched over the tortoiseshell rims of her glasses.

"It's funny," Elaine said. "You hardly ever talk about Justin, but whenever the subject comes up I get the feeling something is going on between you two. What gives?"

There were times when Kit hated Elaine's seemingly uncanny ability to read her mind. This was one of them. "You never did say what kind of pizza you wanted," she hedged.

"Changing the subject will do you no good," Lori said, closing in for the kill. "You know we'll get you sooner or later, so why prolong the torture?"

"I don't know what you guys are talking about!" She dropped her voice to an indignant whisper. "There's absolutely *nothing* going on between Justin and me!"

"Then why are we whispering?" Elaine hissed back.

Kit rolled her eyes. "For heaven's sake! Will you *please* cut it out? He might *hear* you."

"Okay, okay." Elaine gave Kit's hand a conciliatory pat. "Don't get so excited. We were just kidding. You don't have to tell us about Justin if you don't want to."

"There's nothing to tell!"

Lori smiled knowingly. She picked a straw from the basket by the cash register and slowly peeled the paper off. "Whatever you say, Kit."

"Honestly!" Kit cried, holding in the giggle that threatened to erupt at any moment. She always giggled when she was nervous.

Lori and Elaine exchanged looks. "We believe you," Elaine said. "You don't have to convince *us*."

Lori twisted the straw around her finger. "I think he's cute. He sits behind me in Civics, but you'd hardly know it. He's so quiet."

"Maybe he's the strong, silent type," Elaine suggested. "Anyway, I've seen him around, and you're right . . . he *is* cute." She was looking at Kit with those X-ray eyes again. "It just seems so odd, that's all. Here you are, spending all this time with someone as cute as Justin and he hardly gets a footnote."

"Cool it!" Kit hissed. "I think I hear my boss."

Mr. Watkins stuck his head out of his office, wearing a suspicious look that took in Kit and her two friends.

"I'll have mine with double cheese and plenty of onions," Elaine announced in a loud voice, wearing a perfectly straight face.

It's funny, Kit thought, but Elaine could get away with murder, since no one just looking at her would ever suspect her of anything worse than writing outside the lines on an essay paper. Even Mr. Watkins' scowl melted slightly at the sight of Elaine in her plaid slacks and brown turtleneck, peering thoughtfully up at the menu.

Lori, on the other hand, would have been a dead giveaway if her boss had been paying closer attention. Lori's cheeks were a mottled red as she gave her order in a voice that was scarcely above a whisper. "Diet Pepsi, please."

Kit watched Mr. Watkins sidle back into his office, and she breathed a sigh of relief.

"We'd better cut out before we get you in any more trouble," Elaine said.

"What about your pizza?" Kit wanted to know.

"Oh, that. Never mind. I was just trying to get you off the hook. Besides, I hate onions."

Lori followed Elaine to the door. "Bye, Kit," she

said as she ducked out. A moment later, she popped her head back inside and called, "Give my regards to you-know-who!"

Kit shook her fist, pretending to be angry. "I'll get you for this!" she called out, nearly choking on her laughter. "Someday, I'll pay you back the same way!"

Elaine, who was always lamenting the fact that there was no special boy in her life, answered with a sigh, "I can hardly wait."

Kit was supposed to get off at six, but by quarter past, Kit still hadn't finished cleaning up. She couldn't exactly run out on Mr. Watkins, either, after the lecture he'd given her for being late. She glanced at the clock in dismay. She would never make it in time for her lesson at this rate.

To top everything off, there was Justin, ignoring her as usual. Kit felt like screaming. Instead, she picked up speed as she was wiping the counter. Before she knew it, she'd plowed right into Justin, who was in the midst of opening a gigantic can of tomato sauce. She leaped back as if electrified. Her elbow caught the can, knocking it over.

"Oh!" she squealed as a geyser of tomato sauce spewed across the counter, drenching them both and forming a bright red lake in the middle of the floor. Kit stared at it in shocked disbelief for several seconds before the realization of what she'd done sank in.

She clapped her hands to both flaming cheeks,

uttering a second, softer "Oh!" She looked up at Justin. "I can't believe it. You must think I'm the world's biggest klutz!"

"Only the second biggest," Justin said gently, the corners of his wide mouth turning up in a slow smile. "You're looking at Number One. I can't walk by a lamp cord without tripping over it."

He was actually joking with her! Kit couldn't believe it. He wasn't mad at her. He didn't even seem very upset.

"I—I'd better get the mop," she stammered, too flustered to flirt for a change. "If Mr. Watkins sees this, he'll fire me for sure."

"I'll help you," he said.

"It wasn't your fault. You don't have to—" Kit started to protest, but Justin had already vanished into the storeroom. He reappeared a minute later, carrying a bucket and two mops.

Kit was flooded with warm gratitude. How could he be so nice when she was causing him so much trouble? Especially when he'd made it obvious before that he didn't even like her.

She covered her confusion by attacking the puddle vigorously with her mop. "I really do appreciate this," she said shyly after a few minutes. "If I don't get out of here pretty soon, I'll miss my dance lesson."

"You're a dancer?" Justin asked in surprise.

"I know," Kit laughed. "After this, you're probably wondering how someone as klutzy as me could be a dancer. I just want you to know, I'm not this bad all the time."

"Actually, I was thinking you'd make a good dancer. Most of the time, you're pretty graceful, the way you walk and all." Now it was Justin's turn to blush. Obviously, he hadn't meant to say all that. Ducking his head in embarrassment, he quickly added, "Anyway, that explains the mystery."

"What mystery?"

"I wondered why you're always in such a big hurry to get out of here every Monday."

Kit felt the knot in her stomach loosen. So he had noticed something about her! "I guess there's a lot about each other we don't know," she said cautiously, as she squeezed her dripping mop into the bucket.

"Yeah, well . . . that's how it goes sometimes. With you, I always figured . . . oh, never mind." He stopped, fixing her with a mildly puzzled look, as if he, too, was thinking that she no longer fit the image he'd formed of her. "Listen, Kit, why don't I drop you off at your lesson on my way home? I wouldn't want you to be late."

Kit's heart began to beat very quickly. "Oh, that'd be fan— are you sure it's not too much trouble?"

Justin laughed, a low easy sound that fit perfectly with the rest of him. "The truth is, you'd be doing *me* a favor. I'm afraid if I'm the only one walking around out there covered in tomato sauce, people are going to look at me funny. At least this way, I won't be the only target."

41

In spite of the fact that she was already late for her lesson, as well as being drenched in tomato sauce, Kit suddenly felt lighthearted. A few minutes later, as Justin was letting her off in front of her dance studio, he reached across the seat to touch her hand. Her heart soared. She could feel the warm imprint of his fingers even after he drew away.

"I'd like to see you dance sometime," he said.

"I'm doing a routine for Senior Vaudeville in a few weeks," she told him. "Are you going?"

"I wasn't really planning on it, but I guess I'll have to make a point of it now."

Kit scrambled out of the car before he could see how red her face had turned. "Bye!" she called.

Justin waved as he pulled away from the curb. Kit stood watching until the Toyota's blinking taillight disappeared around the corner. Then she wheeled with a little skip, bounding up the front steps two at a time.

Chapter Five

Kit peeled back the foil on her TV dinner. "Yuck," she muttered.

Tonight, she wasn't in the mood for Swanson's Salisbury Steak. Tonight, she felt like having something really special. Something home-cooked—like pot roast and mashed potatoes, apple crisp and vanilla ice cream. When Janice was in the right mood, she was a terrific cook. The trouble was, she was hardly ever in the right mood. Mostly they ate take-out, or threw together something quick like salad, or soup and sandwiches. Tonight, Janice wasn't even home. Kit had returned from her lesson to find a note from her mother stuck on the refrigerator: "Gone to the movies with Doug. There's food in the fridge. Don't wait up! Love, Mom."

Kit left the TV dinner untouched on the kitchen table, grabbing an apple instead. She went back into the living room and plopped down on the carpet to do leg pulls while she watched the rest of the movie that was on. She'd seen it before—it was an old one called *A Summer Place,* starring a couple of once-upon-a-time teen idols named Troy Donahue and Sandra Dee. The last time, watching it with Janice, she'd cried at the end, only she had pretended it was because she had something in her eye. It seemed so dumb, somehow, crying over a corny old movie about two kids who in real life were middle-aged by now. She'd seen Troy Donahue on the "Merv Griffin Show," and he was practically bald.

Alex called just at the part where Sandra Dee finds out she's pregnant.

"Hi," Alex said. "Am I interrupting anything? You sound like you're out of breath."

"I'm just doing my exercises," Kit told her. "I missed the warm-up half of my lesson today, so I'm a little stiff."

Alex groaned in commiseration. "I know how you feel. Today when I was practicing my dives, I came out of one too late and practically did a belly flop. My whole body feels like one giant bruise. Hey, what's all that noise? Do you have company?"

Kit reached over and turned the sound down. "It's just the TV. I'm watching this movie about two teen-agers who want to get married, but their parents hate each other and won't let them."

"Sounds vaguely familiar," Alex said in a deadpan voice. "I think we read it in English last year.

Romeo and Juliet, right?"

"Wait, I haven't gotten to the best part yet. You see, they do it this one time, then she gets pregnant, so then they *have* to get married . . ."

"God," Alex cut in with a disgusted sigh. "Don't you have anything better to do than watch that kind of stuff?"

"As a matter of fact, I don't. Mom's not home and I don't feel like doing homework. You want to come over? We could play Monopoly or something."

"Can't. I'm going out with Danny. He's taking me roller skating. Do you believe it? We swam forty laps apiece this afternoon, not counting the dive practice, and he wants to go roller skating. It's incredible! I think I must be going steady with the Six Million Dollar Man.

Kit thought about Justin. "It must be nice to have someone special."

"I'll let you know after tonight," Alex laughed. "That is, if I live to tell it."

Kit knew she was only kidding. More likely, it was Alex's idea to go roller skating. It was a good thing she'd found someone who could keep up with her. Kit remembered last year, when Alex had gone out with Jim Bradley for a while. Jim was class president, sort of a bookworm who preferred reading to jogging. Finally, he told Alex that he had to stop seeing her—if he didn't, he was going to drop dead of exhaustion.

"You ought to go out tonight yourself," Alex urged. "Watching that kind of stuff can get depressing."

"No, it's not, really. In the end, they get married and have the baby."

"Ugh. I'm not getting married until I'm at least thirty."

Kit laughed. "You sound like Joanne Burdick, this girl in my Chemistry class. She told me she's never getting married. She doesn't think it's possible to sustain a meaningful relationship with someone who'd have to see her every morning without her makeup."

"At least that's better than worrying about morning mouth," Alex said. "I know a girl who says that when she gets married, she's keeping a roll of Certs under her pillow all the time. Then she'll never have to worry about bad breath."

"What if her husband has it?"

"I guess she hasn't considered that possibility. Besides, dream men never have bad breath. What would be the point of fantasizing if they did?"

Kit decided she didn't want a dream man. She wanted someone real—someone she could talk to. She wouldn't care if he saw her without her makeup. She wouldn't care if his hair stuck up in cowlicks some days . . . or if he tripped over lamp cords once in a while. An image of Justin bobbed along the surface of her thoughts. She hugged it to her, reliving the warmth of his touch, remembering the thoughtful way his eyes had regarded her when they were talking.

"I've gotta go," Alex announced abruptly. "Danny's car just pulled into the driveway. Take it easy, okay?"

"You, too."

"Ha!" was her breathless reply.

After she'd hung up, Kit stretched out on her side to do leg lifts. With her ear pressed to the floor, she could hear snatches of conversation drifting up from the apartment directly below. A mother was arguing with her son, telling him that if he didn't like the way she fixed liver, he could fix it himself next time. The boy said he didn't hate the way she fixed it, he just hated liver, period.

Kit sat up, suddenly disgusted with herself for having nothing better to do than eavesdrop on the people below. Why was it so quiet in here, anyway? She turned the sound back up on the TV to drown out the silence that pulsed about her.

When the phone rang a few minutes later, Kit snatched it up eagerly, hoping it was Lori or Elaine. She'd thought about calling one of them herself, but she knew that Elaine was busy studying for her SAT's, and Lori had said she and her mom might go shopping.

Kit was startled by the sound of a deep male voice. "Kit?"

She nearly dropped the phone in surprise. Her heart climbed into her throat. "Justin?"

He laughed, that same easy sound that rippled over her like a caress. "You sound surprised."

"I—I just wasn't expecting you to call," she stammered.

47

"Actually, it took me sort of by surprise, too," he said. "I mean, before I got to know you a little better, I didn't think—oh, what am I saying? You see, I get nervous and all this garbage just starts pouring out. What I really meant to say was— today was nice."

Now it was Kit's turn to laugh. "You call getting tomato sauce dumped all over you *nice*?"

"Well, okay, I guess we both could've done without that part. What I meant was, it was nice talking to you. It seems funny—we've been working together for a few months, but we haven't really gotten to know each other."

"It's not easy when you're up to your elbows in pizza dough all the time," Kit said, mentally forgiving him on the spot for all his former standoffishness.

He cleared his throat. "What I was wondering was—would you like to go to a movie sometime? Or if you don't feel like a movie, we could—"

"I'd *love* to go to a movie," Kit interrupted in a burst of enthusiasm. "How about tonight? I'm not doing anything, and we still have time to catch the nine o'clock show."

"Great!" Justin said it in a way that made her tingle all over with goose bumps. "Fifteen minutes okay?"

"I'll meet you out in front," she said, giving him the address.

Not until she'd hung up did the great bubble of excitement that had been swelling up inside her burst open. In the middle of the living room, she did a flying cartwheel that landed her on the couch in a breathless sprawl.

"All right!" she cried, tossing a throw pillow high into the air. "All *right!*"

By a quarter to nine, Kit was stationed on the front steps of the apartment building, waiting eagerly for Justin to arrive. She couldn't remember the last time she'd been this nervous before a date. In the past fifteen minutes, she'd changed clothes three times, finally settling on a pair of short green culottes and a low-necked peasant blouse. She wasn't taking any chances this time. Somehow—she didn't exactly know why—she'd managed to snag Justin's interest. Tonight, she was making sure it stayed.

She ran the tip of her tongue over her lips, tasting the strawberry lip gloss she'd put on. Justin never looked at her the way other boys did. Did he think she was pretty? Or would he be too busy staring at the pimple on her forehead (which she'd just discovered to her horror) to notice anything else? God, why did she have to suggest he take her out *tonight* of all nights? She should have *remembered* that her hair hadn't been washed in two days, and that her nail polish was chipped. Why was she always leaping into things without thinking?

Nevertheless, Kit felt a rush of excitement when she saw Justin's Toyota pull up. She took a deep breath to calm her fluttering nerves as she walked out to meet him. *Okay, Kit, this is it.*

Don't blow it this time. Give it everything you've got.

"Hi!" he greeted her as she scooted in beside him.

"Hi there, yourself," she cooed in her movie-star-cool voice, adding with a giggle, "I hardly recognize you without your apron. I like that sweater. It sort of goes with your eyes. Very sexy."

Justin looked a little uncomfortable, but he smiled anyway. "Thanks." He drove in silence for a couple of minutes. "I thought we could catch the new Woody Allen flick that's playing in Palo Alto. Have you seen it?"

"I'm not really in the mood for comedy tonight. I feel like something romantic—don't you?" she suggested teasingly.

"Uh, sure . . . I guess that's okay. Whatever you want." He didn't sound too enthusiastic, though.

Kit felt a twinge of panic. Maybe he'd changed his mind about her. Maybe he regretted his impulsiveness in asking her out, but was too polite to back out . . .

Whatever the reason, it seemed to Kit that from then on, the evening—like a kite that's gone into a tailspin and can't be coaxed upward again—went steadily downhill. For one thing, the movie she chose wasn't very romantic after all, even though the poster advertising it showed a couple locked in a steamy embrace. Instead, there were a lot of stupid car chases and people getting shot. Kit didn't care about that so much; she was hardly paying attention to the movie anyway. She spent most of the time concentrating on Justin's elbow, which was resting beside hers. Every time he moved, the feathery nap of his sweater grazed her, sending armies of goose bumps skittering up her bare arm. Why didn't he at least hold her hand? She'd managed to brush his fingers several times while they were eating popcorn, but he hadn't taken the hint. Kit thought about her conversation with Alex that evening. Maybe she had bad breath! At one point, she blew surreptitiously into her palm while pretending to yawn, but the only thing she could tell was that her hand smelled like popcorn.

By the time the show got out, Kit was close to desperation. She was surprised when Justin—who had barely said two words to her during the movie—suggested they go get something to eat. She decided he really must be starving. Why else would he have suggested it?

He took her to the Burger Palace, a place down the block from the theater. Inside, it was bright and noisy. The smell of frying meat hung in the air. Practically everyone stopped at the Palace after the movies, not just the kids her age, so Kit shouldn't have been surprised when she spotted her mother in one of the booths. Janice didn't see her, though. She was too busy talking to the man seated next to her. He was good-looking, but in a way that didn't appeal to Kit—dark and stocky, with lots of springy black hair—and when he smiled, she saw he had more teeth than the

51

whole Osmond family put together. Kit didn't have to look hard to see that they were holding hands.

Suddenly, everything that had gone wrong with the evening backed up on Kit at once. She felt slightly sick. A sour popcorn taste flooded her mouth, and her eyes filled with tears.

Justin touched her arm. "Kit? Are you okay? We don't have to stay if you don't feel like it."

She looked up at him in panic. Justin had never met her mother. How could she introduce him now? It would seem so incredibly awkward. Kit didn't even know this man who was acting as though he were practically engaged to Janice! What would Justin think?

Kit realized that Justin was staring at her with a puzzled expression. She opened her mouth to say something bright and false that would cover up the way she was feeling, but the words stuck in her throat. Instead, she spun about with a tiny choked cry, blindly pushing her way outside.

Chapter Six

"Kit!"

She'd made it no more than halfway to the car when she felt him snatch her arm from behind. Kit wheeled to face Justin, overwhelmed by an odd mixture of relief and embarrassment. He was panting and his face was flushed from the exertion of racing after her.

"You're pretty fast, you know that?" he said, taking her gently by the shoulders. "Do you want to tell me what all this is about? You don't have to, but if it'd help, I'm a good listener."

How could she explain to him when she didn't even know herself why she was so upset? Kit slowly shook her head. Why should he care? It was obvious from the way he'd been acting all night that he was sorry he'd asked her out. Nevertheless Justin's show of sympathy touched her so unexpectedly that she burst into tears.

Kit didn't care that they were standing in the middle of a brightly lit parking lot where anyone could see them. Apparently, Justin didn't either. He pulled her into his arms without a word, and for a time she was grateful just to burrow into the warm, fuzzy cove of his chest while she gave in to her sobs. She was barely conscious of the headlights sweeping over them as cars pulled out.

Finally, she took a deep breath and lifted her head. "God, you must think I'm awful."

"No . . . I don't," he said softly.

Kit was jolted out of her misery by the gentle sincerity of his response. She gave a little laugh that backfired into a hiccough. "How can you say that? First I spill tomato sauce on you, then I cry all over your sweater for no good reason."

"I'm sure you had a good reason."

Now that the storm had passed, Kit was starting to feel slightly ridiculous. "Maybe. I don't know. You wouldn't happen to have a Kleenex, would you?"

He pulled a folded white square from his back pocket. "Will a handkerchief do?"

She blew her nose, then looked up at him with a sheepish smile. "I should have known you were the type to carry around handkerchiefs. How come you're so organized and I'm such a—" she lifted her arms in a gesture of despair "—a hopeless wreck?" She blew her nose again. "And why is it in the movies when someone cries the only thing that comes out is tears?"

He laughed. "I guess because life isn't like the

movies."

They were standing just outside the cone of bright violet light cast by an arc lamp. Justin's gray eyes looked almost black. They were so close, the toe of one of his sneakers was touching her foot.

Justin cupped his hand under her chin, lifting her face to meet his gaze. "Do you feel like talking about it?"

Kit nodded, suddenly feeling that anything she said to Justin would be okay. She followed him back to the car, where they sat and talked for what seemed like hours. She'd never been this comfortable with a boy before. It was funny, she thought, because the only thing he did was hold her hand, yet she felt so close to him. She told Justin about Janice, and the man at the table, Doug Whatsisname, and how she felt about her mother sometimes. Things she'd never dreamed of admitting—even to herself—just poured right out. Justin listened with an intent expression, never once laughing or acting disgusted.

"I know how you feel," he said when she was finished. "My parents split up a couple of years ago. Since then, my dad doesn't seem like the same person sometimes."

"You live with your father?" she asked.

Justin nodded. "Everybody figured it'd be better this way. We all sat down and talked about it. You know—calm and rational. My whole family is like that, calm and rational. Once, when I was a little kid I broke this very fancy dish of my mother's and she just said, 'I knew that was going to happen one of these days. I'm almost glad it did, so now I can quit worrying about it.' "

Kit laughed. "I see what you mean."

"So there we were, all of us sitting around this table in a Japanese restaurant trying to decide what to do about me. My parents were eating raw fish. I was getting sick. To this day, I can't look at a piece of fish without getting sick."

"Me neither, and I don't even have your excuse. What did they finally decide?"

"Well, my mom travels a lot, so living with her wouldn't have been the best thing, even though we get along really well. She's a filmmaker. She produces documentary films, and is always going to places like Kenya or some fjord in Norway for a couple of months at a time."

"Sounds exciting."

"It is. For her. The trouble is, I can't go with her because of school, and being stuck at home alone all the time gets to be a drag when you don't have any brothers or sisters to keep you company."

Kit knew what that was like, all right. "It's the same with me," she said. "What's it like living with your dad?"

Justin shrugged. "Okay, I guess. Sometimes, I wish he'd get married again, though. It's weird having a father who goes out on dates all the time. He never used to ask me what I thought of his wardrobe. Now he asks me all the time—what do I think of this shirt or that tie? He wants to know if he looks hip enough. Can you believe it?

56

My own father! Sometimes I wonder who's the parent and who's the kid. The craziest thing is, he's even thinking about getting a hair transplant."

Kit was glad that at least her father was dependably square. She couldn't imagine *him* getting a transplant, even though he was definitely getting a little thin on top. Besides, Vi was always preparing Dad for the inevitable by telling him how much she *loved* bald men.

"It's depressing," she sighed. "I used to look forward to growing up. I used to think that when you got older, your worries about that kind of stuff were pretty much over. But I guess some things never change."

"I don't know," Justin said. "I think it'd probably get boring if you knew exactly who you were and where you were going all the time."

"Don't you?" Kit asked in surprise.

Justin always seemed so sure of himself . . . in an unobtrusive way. If there was one thing she hated, it was people who ran around spouting off about how *together* they were as a result of some book they'd read or a weekend seminar they went to. With Justin, it was just obvious; he didn't have to talk about it.

He snorted. "That's a laugh. The only thing I know for sure about myself is that I want to be a doctor. That's why I'm working at this crummy job. I'm saving up for college. I want to go to Stanford—it has one of the best pre-med programs around." He grinned. "So some day when

I'm operating on someone I can think about all the pizza I had to cut up to get there."

"That's the way I feel about dancing," Kit confided. "I love it and never have any doubts. I just wish I could feel so sure about the rest of my life." She looked at Justin, finally screwing up her courage to ask the question that had been in the back of her mind all night. "Justin, why did you ask me out? I couldn't help wondering if you were sorry you did. You seemed . . . I don't know, kind of distant."

"I guess I was—but only at first." He squeezed her hand. "Kit, the truth is, I—I never know what to say when you're acting that way."

Kit felt her stomach plunge. "*What* way?" she asked in an agony of embarrassment.

"The Marilyn Monroe bit. All that teasing around stuff. You don't need it, Kit. It's not really you."

"I wanted to make you like me," she confessed, wavering on the edge of tears again.

"You don't have to *make* me like you," he said. "I do already. Especially now."

"Now?" Kit squeaked. She had a sudden image of what she must look like—her makeup smeared under her eyes, her face blotchy and red from crying. "God, I must be the world's biggest mess!"

Justin laughed, slipping his arms around her. "Maybe so, but remember, I'm funny that way. I happen to like messes."

"Now look who's teasing!"

"Teasing is fine . . . in small doses."

But clearly Justin wasn't teasing as he caught her to him in a slow, gentle kiss.

Kit felt as if she were swimming underwater. There was a rushing in her ears. The tiniest movement became a ballet—when he brought his fingers to her face, brushing them lightly across her cheek; when she wound her arms around his neck to pull him closer. Kit could feel her heart thudding in the pit of her stomach.

It was nice . . . so nice . . .

She was surprised, when they drew apart, to realize that she hadn't wanted the kiss to end. It was the first time she could remember feeling that way.

Chapter Seven

"What do you think of this one?" Lori held up a pale blue formal with a ruffled hem.

Kit stepped back to get a better look, and barely missed colliding with a plump gray-haired woman loaded down with shopping bags. Other shoppers swirled about her, wearing harried expressions. Macy's during a Saturday morning sale wasn't the place to be if you were looking for rest and relaxation, Kit concluded silently.

"Well . . . it matches your eyes," she said, "but I'm not sure about the ruffles. Unless you want to look like Little Bo-Peep."

Lori sighed as she stuffed it back on the rack. "Maybe it fits my personality. Honestly, I don't even know why I'm going to this homecoming dance. I'm sure Ben only asked me to be nice. After all, he's head of the dance committee—he probably had to make sure all the nominees have dates."

"You're absolutely right," Alex said, her brown eyes dancing with mischief, "Poor Ben. Stuck for a whole night with the most gorgeous girl at Glenwood High. I hope he can handle the embarrassment if you get elected Queen."

Kit smiled in sympathy as Lori ducked behind the dress rack. She knew how Lori felt. Sometimes, it was hard to see yourself the way others did. Most of the time, she was so busy concentrating on the *bad* things about herself, that she never even noticed the good.

Right now, though, the good outweighed the bad. She felt terrific. How could she *not* feel terrific when she was going to the Homecoming Ball with the most wonderful boy in the world? Kit had been walking on air ever since Justin phoned two nights ago to ask her.

"At least you have a *date*," Elaine said to Lori. Her expression was wistful as she plucked a dress off the rack and held it up to her. "If I weren't on the dance committee, I wouldn't be going at all."

"*Lots* of people are going stag," Kit reassured her. "You'll have a great time anyway."

"Sure," Alex said. "Danny says half the boys on the team don't have dates."

Elaine laughed. "Great. It helps to know I'm in good company. Maybe we could form an organization—Dateless Anonymous." She replaced the dress after examining herself in the mirror. "When will someone design a formal that looks good with glasses?"

61

They'd been shopping for dresses most of the morning, but Kit wasn't as discouraged as Elaine. She was sure she'd find the right dress eventually. If she could find love in a parking lot, then anything was possible.

Lori popped out from behind a rack of sequined tops. She was grinning triumphantly as she held up a whisper of a dress in a soft shade of rose.

"Kit! This would look *fantastic* on you. The minute I saw it, I just knew."

Kit had to agree—it was beautiful. And the color was perfect for her fair complexion. Not too sexy, either. Just sexy enough. Justin would love it.

Once again, Elaine appeared to be reading her mind. "Lori's right," she piped in. "It's perfect for you. Justin *will* love it."

"Justin who?" Lori teased. Earlier in the day, she'd threatened to stuff her ears with cotton if she heard Kit say his name one more time.

Kit blushed, both pleased and embarrassed. "Will you guys cut it out? You're beginning to give me a complex! Maybe I shouldn't tell you any more about my love life."

"If you didn't tell us, who *would* you tell?" Elaine wanted to know.

Kit thought about it for a moment. "Maybe I'd write it all down in a diary."

"You should never tell your deepest darkest secrets to your diary," Lori warned. "What if your mother found it?"

Kit didn't want to tell them that her sex life would seem pretty tame by her mother's standards.

Elaine groaned. "What's worse is your little sister finding your diary. That's what happened to me. There's this one part in it she'll never let me forget."

"What is it?" Kit asked, intrigued by the idea of Elaine having a secret life.

"I wrote that I thought I must be adopted, since nobody in my family looks like me."

"What's wrong with that?" Lori wanted to know. "Lots of kids think that."

"I also said I suspected my real mother might be Katharine Hepburn, since a lot of people have told me I sort of look like her," Elaine confessed sheepishly.

Lori started to giggle. "You didn't!"

"I was only nine! Blame it on my fertile imagination."

Alex grabbed Kit by the hand. "Come on, we can try on our dresses at the same time." She was clutching an armload of dresses in every shade of the rainbow.

The two of them headed for the dressing room, leaving Lori and Elaine to continue what Elaine called Mission Impossible. Kit exchanged looks with Alex while the blue-haired saleslady sifted through their pile with a suspicious expression. Kit had to press her lips together to keep from laughing. She noticed Alex was having trouble keeping a straight face, too. Finally, they were given a number. They ducked into the nearest empty cubicle, barely making it in time before they exploded into wild giggles.

"Why do salesladies always look at you like you're about to shoplift everything in sight?" Alex wanted to know. "Maybe I should have told her not to worry—that I'm an international jewel thief and I wouldn't stoop to shoplifting at Macy's."

"Maybe *she's* the jewel thief. Being a saleslady is just one of her many disguises . . ."

"Ssshh," Alex hissed, "She'll hear you. Once she knows we're on to her, we'll be out of here in our underwear!"

When her laughing attack had subsided, Kit peeled off her jeans and top, and slipped the dress over her head. The silken fabric rippled along her skin in one cool, delicious shudder. She stared at herself in the mirror. It was perfect! A sigh of wonder escaped her as she took in the delicately draped bodice, the long slender skirt that ended in a single row of tiny ruching. Kit twirled about in a flutter of tags. It was love at first sight.

"Justin's going to faint when he sees you," Alex said, standing back to get a better look. "You look . . . well, let's put it this way—if I weren't such a good friend, I'd probably murder you on the spot out of pure jealousy."

Kit smiled in amusement. "What do you have to be jealous about? You know Danny won't be looking at anybody but you. He's crazy about you."

Alex yanked a dress over her head, muttering

impatiently when the zipper caught in her hair. Finally, she freed it, her head emerging with a crackle of electricity that sent her hair flying in all directions.

"Maybe Danny isn't as crazy about me as everyone thinks," she said, her expression darkening.

Kit waited for Alex to tell her what was bothering her, but Alex didn't say anything more. She was great at handing out advice, Kit knew. Asking for it was much harder.

"Did you two have a fight?" Kit prodded gently.

"Not exactly. No, I wouldn't call it a fight. The whole thing is really crazy. They could probably put it on *That's Incredible!*"

Kit resisted the impulse to smile. Alex would probably crack jokes at her own funeral. Instead of laughing, she squeezed Alex's hand sympathetically.

"Come on, it couldn't be that bad."

"Do you want to hear the whole gory truth?"

"Sure. Isn't that what friends are for—to listen to gory truths you couldn't tell anyone else?"

Alex had discarded one dress and was zipping her way into another. "Last night Danny and I were over at his sister's apartment—you remember Ellen, don't you? Well, Danny is supposed to be watering her plants for her while she's on vacation. So there we were, all alone in this apartment—did I mention she has a waterbed? The apartment's kind of small, so it's right in the middle of the living room. You can't miss it."

"Alex," Kit interrupted, "What *happened*?"

"Nothing. Oh, we fooled around a little. The usual kind of stuff. Then—I don't know what came over me, Kit, I really don't—but all of a sudden I felt like doing it."

"You mean *It*?" Kit was mildly shocked, but at the same time wildly curious.

"Don't worry," Alex said. "We didn't. But it's not what you think. Danny's the one who said no."

"I thought he wanted to."

"So did I. I was hurt at first. I felt like I'd made this really huge decision, and he was throwing it right back in my face. Then later on we talked about it. He said it wasn't that he didn't *want* to do it—he just suddenly realized what a big step it was. He said maybe if he didn't love me it'd be different. He's afraid we'll get too involved, I guess. I think what he really means is, if we do it once we're going to want to do it all the time. Maybe we won't want to do anything else—stuff like getting ready for college and training for meets." She shrugged, examining her reflection in a fluffy pink formal that clashed horribly with the color of her hair and skin. "The thing is, I know exactly how he feels, because it's how *I* feel. But it seems weird somehow, having the tables turned."

It seemed strange to Kit, too. She'd always thought guys had it pretty much together in that department. At least, they seemed to *know* what they wanted, even if they didn't always get it. The idea that a boy could be just as insecure and uncertain about sex as a girl was new and disturbing. Did Justin sometimes feel that way? she wondered. How would he react if given the opportunity to do It with her?

"Maybe Danny's right," Kit said. "It *is* an awfully big step."

"I know. And in a way I'm glad we didn't, but at the same time I can't help feeling sort of rejected. If I were *Playboy* centerfold material, maybe he wouldn't have been so quick to put on the brakes."

"Now *that* is the dumbest thing I've ever heard you say!" Kit flared in loyal indignation.

Alex gave in to a sheepish grin. "I guess I wouldn't look so terrific with my navel stapled, anyway." She stripped off the pink dress with a snort of disgust. "Come on, let's get out of here. None of this stuff would win me any prizes. You're lucky you hit it right on the first try. You're getting the dress, aren't you?"

Kit had been so caught up in Alex's dilemma, she'd forgotten to look at the price tag. She glanced at it now, feeling a wave of disappointment when she saw it was too much. *Much* too much. Janice had given her fifty dollars to spend—more than she could afford, Kit knew. Even with the extra twenty of her own she'd brought, it wouldn't be enough.

"I—I'm not sure," she stammered, ashamed to tell Alex the truth. She hated never having enough. They weren't poor, but extras were definitely a thing of the past. She felt a wave of hot frustration, which she quickly squashed down. "I'll have to think about it. Maybe I'll see one I like even better."

"Are you kidding? Believe me, Kit, this dress is absolutely per—" Alex stopped, realization dawning on her face. As tactfully as possible, she said, "Look, if it's too much, I can loan you the difference. I have all that money I saved up from lifeguarding last summer . . ."

"No," Kit said, quietly but firmly. "Don't think I don't appreciate it. I really do. I just can't. Please understand."

Alex nodded after a minute. Kit was glad to see she really did understand. Borrowing from friends was fine—as long as it was a two-way street. But Kit knew she could never return the favor.

Suddenly, she didn't feel so terrible anymore. What was one dress compared to a friend like Alex?

Janice was doing her yoga exercises on the living room carpet when Kit arrived home from her shopping expedition. Her mother sat very straight, the soles of her feet tucked together, her knees pressed to the floor. In a leotard, Kit thought, she had nothing to hide. Janice had the figure of a teen-ager.

Her mother looked up, brushing a wisp of honey-blond hair from her eyes. "Hi! You were gone so long I figured you must've turned every

68

store in the shopping center inside out. Any luck?"

"Not really." Kit watched her mother slowly straighten her legs, then bend over and touch her forehead to her knees. "We finally found the perfect dress for Elaine, though. Sort of Victorian style. Very elegant, but not too flashy. It even looks good with her glasses, but Elaine's going to try and get through the evening without them. She's determined to look stunning, even if she has to trip all over everything to do it."

"That's nice." Kit could see that Janice's mind was elsewhere. On Doug maybe? Her stomach clenched at the thought. "Kit, honey, about dinner . . . would you mind whipping up something just for yourself? Doug and I thought we'd go out."

Kit was annoyed. "You went out with him last night, too."

"That's true." A guilty expression flitted across Janice's flushed face. "Listen, honey, I have an idea. Why don't you come with us? It'd be fun. We could go out for some Chinese food. Remember that place we went to on your birthday—the one with the funny fortune cookies?"

"Thanks, Mom, but I think I'll skip it," Kit answered in a tight voice. "I have a lot of homework to do."

Janice looked hurt. "Is it Doug? Don't you like him?"

Kit had met Doug the night before. To tell the truth, he'd been perfectly polite. He asked her all the normal questions—did she like school? What was she planning to do after she graduated? Had she picked out a college yet?

No, it wasn't that she disliked Doug. Given the chance, she could probably get to like him as well as Peter or Hugh or any of the others before that. Whether or not she liked Doug wasn't the point. Why should she try to get to know him if she didn't know whether he was even going to be around a month from now?

Kit sighed. What was the use? She could see her mother was hurt, and that only made her feel worse. Janice wasn't trying to be mean. Kit knew things weren't so easy for her, either.

Fighting to control her anger, she said, "Sure, Doug's okay. That's not it. I really do have a lot of homework."

"Well, okay then." Janice relaxed her worried expression a little. "But if you change your mind, you're still invited. We'd love to have you. Oh, by the way, there's a letter from your dad. I left it on your dresser."

Kit flew into her room. She found the letter propped against a jar of cold cream, and tore it open eagerly. It had been a while since she'd heard from her father. It was easier to telephone, he always said—except that he didn't do that much either, now that it was long distance.

There was a note inside, folded around a check. Kit looked at the check first—it was for fifty dollars! She could hardly believe it! The note said: "Dear Kit, Thought this might come in handy.

You know I wish it could be a million. You're worth every penny. Love, Daddy."

She thought about the dress she could now afford to buy. It was as if somehow he'd known, even though she realized that was impossible. Trembling with emotion, she sank down on her bed, still clutching the check.

I love you, Daddy, she mouthed silently.

Chapter Eight

"You weren't kidding about being a terrific dancer," Justin whispered in Kit's ear.

She shivered as his arm tightened around her waist. They moved to the slow, measured rhythm as if they'd been dancing together all their lives. Kit felt perfectly at ease. In the past, she had never really been able to relax, even if her partner was a good dancer. She was always uncomfortably aware of the boy's body crushed up against hers—wondering why he was sweating so much, or how to tell him in a nice way to stop squeezing her so hard. With Justin, it wasn't like that at all. Dancing with him was as natural as breathing, to coin a favorite phrase of her mother's.

Kit thought about the times they'd been together since their first date. She always felt relaxed and happy around Justin, though never quite as romantic as this. Justin had sensed that she needed to warm up slowly, so all they'd done up until now was a little kissing and lots of hand-holding.

Since they'd arrived at the dance, Kit had lost track of time. She was caught up in the magic of the evening and never wanted it to end. This year's theme was "Top Hat," and thanks to Elaine's artistic touch, the decorations were fabulous. The multiuse room had been transformed into a 1920's style nightclub, with a silver and black color scheme. Cutouts of top hats and canes decorated the walls alongside life-sized posters of old-time movie-musical stars like Fred Astaire and Ginger Rogers. Candles burned in colored jars on the tables, their light reflected in a thousand sparkling points by the slowly twirling glitter ball that hung from the ceiling. A full-piece band played old-fashioned music mixed in with popular new hits.

"You're pretty terrific yourself," Kit whispered back. "And not just at dancing."

"Oh?" Justin lifted an eyebrow. He'd told her he was beginning to get used to her teasing—as long as it didn't get too out of hand.

Kit giggled. "You're terrific at making pizza, for one thing . . . and cleaning up after klutzes, for another."

"Is that all?" he asked, pretending to be disappointed.

"Well, maybe one or two other things." *Like kissing,* she longed to say, only she didn't dare. Justin might take it the wrong way. "Do you have any specialties I don't know about?"

"You mean like sword swallowing or lion taming—that kind of stuff?" His gray eyes twinkled with laughter.

"Nothing that exotic. I was thinking more along the lines of—hey, do you play chess?"

"Are you kidding? I've been playing since I was a little kid. Don't tell me you're a chess freak, too?"

"Alex's brother taught me. He's practically in Bobby Fischer's league. Of course, he's impossible to beat, but I don't mind. It makes it more of a challenge."

Justin shook his head. "I can't believe you didn't tell me this before. Think of all the times I could've beaten you by now."

"It's better this way," Kit said with a soft sigh of contentment. "Getting to know each other a little bit at a time. Don't you think?"

Justin didn't answer, he just pulled her closer, brushing his lips across her cheek. Kit's stomach did a slow somersault. Her skin tingled where he'd kissed her. At this moment, the power he had to turn her to jelly with the slightest touch was beginning to unnerve her. If it was this bad now, what would it be like when they were alone?

When the dance ended, they drifted over to the refreshment table, which had been decorated to resemble a twenties-style speakeasy. She spotted Elaine, who was busy ladling out punch. In her Victorian-style dress, with her hair swept back in a French knot, Kit thought Elaine looked stunning.

"You look great," Kit told her. "Even with your glasses."

Elaine blushed, poking self-consciously at them. "Thanks. I tried going without, but I couldn't see a thing. I was mixing up a batch of punch and accidentally dumped in a bottle of lemon juice instead of soda." A grin came sneaking in, despite her attempt to hide it. "You should've seen the look on Marcia Connors' face when she tasted it!"

Kit couldn't resist smiling herself. Marcia was one of the nominees for Queen—a real snob, in Kit's opinion. She was one of those every-hair-in-place types who act as if they expect guys to fall all over themselves when they meet her. Unfortunately, most of the time they did.

Elaine handed her a cup of punch. "Don't worry, I fixed it. We're calling it 'bathtub ginger ale.' Cute, huh?"

"Speaking of cute—who was that boy I saw you dancing with a little while ago?"

Elaine's color went from pink to scarlet. "Uh . . . nobody. Just a guy."

Kit had waved to Elaine at the time, but she was too entranced to notice. Her partner was very athletic-looking, big and broad-shouldered, with a mop of dark brown hair that curled down around the rumpled collar of his shirt. Everything about him had looked slightly rumpled, in a breezy way, as if he'd just dashed in off the forty-yard line. He wasn't at all what Kit would have picked as Elaine's type.

Elaine quickly changed the subject. "Hey, have you seen Lori? They're about to announce the voting results for Homecoming Queen."

"She's probably hiding in the bathroom," Kit said. She turned to Justin, explaining, "Lori's the shy type."

Justin looked surprised. "You could've fooled me. She always looks so . . ." he searched for the right word ". . . regal, I suppose you'd call it."

"Don't let that fool you," Kit laughed. "It's only the look of well-disguised panic."

Justin squeezed her arm. "Well, I guess that goes to show, you should never judge someone on appearances alone."

His gray eyes were full of special meaning as he gazed at her. Up close, Kit noticed that the very centers of his irises were pinwheeled with splinters of silver-blue. She shivered with sudden emotion, feeling as if Justin could look right through her and read her thoughts. If he really could, would he understand her? She understood so little about herself, how could she expect him to put together all the pieces? It would be like trying to play chess without knowing any of the rules.

Kit and Justin were drifting back onto the dance floor when Kit spotted Alex. She waved, and Alex sailed over, Danny in tow. Kit took in Alex's appearance with a smile of admiration. Alex, as usual, was dressed like nobody else. Not satisfied with the run-of-the-mill formals she'd tried on when they went shopping on Saturday, she finally dragged them all down to Vintage Stuff, an antique clothing store. There, while they were having fun draping themselves in feather boas and campy old mink coats, Alex had fallen madly in love with an old satin dressing gown. It would be *perfect*, she insisted, with a few alterations; she didn't care that it was a *man's* dressing gown, either. But looking at her now, Kit had to admit she did look perfect—perfectly Alex. Kit couldn't help wishing she was a little more like her—confident enough to be her own person, no matter what other people thought.

"Where's Lori?" Alex wanted to know. "Rick Hobart is blowing into the microphone so that must mean he's getting ready to make the big announcement. If Lori ditched out, I'm going to murder her!"

"Down, girl," Danny laughed, draping an arm about Alex's shoulders as if to restrain her. "You promised you'd lay off just this once, remember? Give poor Lori a break. Maybe she'd rather blend in with the wallpaper than be Brooke Shields."

Alex punched his arm lightly, but Kit could see that she didn't mind his teasing. The two of them were always clowning around—except when they were in the water. About diving, they were both dead serious.

"There's no way Lori could be a wallflower, even if she wanted to be," Alex defended her friend. "When you look like Brooke Shields, you're stuck with it."

"Tough luck, huh?" Danny ducked to avoid the next blow. His booming laughter drowned out the crackle of the microphone.

Kit liked Danny. In a lot of ways, he reminded her of Alex. They shared the same healthy tanned look, except that Danny's hair was light brown, streaked with sunny highlights, and his eyes a swimming-pool blue. He could be just as strong-willed as Alex, too. A good thing, Kit thought, since she probably would have steam-rollered anyone less stubborn. This way, the worst that ever happened was an occasional bruise from bumping heads.

"Are they always like this?" Justin whispered, laughing.

"Only when they're getting along," Kit quipped.

Her attention was drawn to the stage. Rick Hobart, the class president, had stopped blowing into the microphone and was now clearing his throat to get everyone's attention. With the amplifier turned up full blast, it sounded like a 747 taking off.

"I know you're all as anxious as I am to hear the results of the voting," he began, doing his Bert Parks imitation, "so I won't keep you in suspense any longer . . ."

Accompanied by a drum roll, he read off the names of the four attending princesses. Marcia Connors was one. She was smiling as she glided up onstage, but Kit could see the disappointment stamped on her features. Clearly, Marcia had expected to win. Lori's name still hadn't been called. Kit felt a twinge of panic on her friend's behalf. Where was she?

There was a pause while the attendants lined up onstage, congratulating each other and blowing kisses to their dates. Then Rick cleared his throat with one last ear-shattering blast.

"Okay, guys, here it is—the big winner. The Homecoming Queen Lori Woodhouse! Lori, where are you?"

Applause broke out, and Kit was gripped by a new fear. What if Lori didn't show? Marcia and her friends would probably say she was too snobbish to want to be queen of a dumb high school prom. Poor Lori! She dreaded gossip the way some people fear a nuclear invasion.

As if sensing Kit's unease, Justin squeezed her hand reassuringly.

Kit relaxed when she spotted a shimmering blond head surface above the crowd. Lori looked absolutely breathtaking in a pale blue dress that floated about her like mist. Her date, Ben Price, a tall basketball player with a spiky blond Rod Stewart haircut, loped along at her side wearing a dazzled, adoring grin. Lori didn't even appear to notice. As she neared, Kit caught the look of sheer panic behind her forced smile. Kit couldn't help feeling a little puzzled. She knew how shy Lori was, but that didn't explain why the slightest bit of attention made her react as if she were being sent before a firing squad. How could anyone as gorgeous as Lori be so deathly afraid of having people look at her?

A moment later, though, Kit forgot her concern over Lori when the band began playing again—a sweet, lilting waltz that drew her into Justin's arms like an invisible magnet.

The song was half over before she was even aware they were dancing.

"Are you sure it's okay—I mean, with your mom not home and all?" Justin paused at the door to Kit's apartment, his gaze sweeping the room, as if he half expected her mother to pop up from behind the sofa at any moment.

"Sure it's okay," Kit said, breezing in ahead of him. "You don't know Mom. She's not exactly the strict type. If anything, I'm more straight than she is. Anyway, we're only going to be listening to records."

"You're lucky," Justin said, sinking down on the couch. "My mother is just the opposite. You'd think she'd be more liberated since she's so independent and all, but she's really uptight about stuff like that. Probably because she and my dad had to get married. She's afraid I'll get some girl pregnant and ruin my life the same way."

"Your mother thinks you ruined her life?" Kit asked indignantly.

"Not exactly. She's always saying she's glad she had me and all. I just get the feeling she would've preferred to wait until she finished doing everything else she wanted to do and was ready to settle down."

"When would that have been?" Kit asked.

"Oh, when she's about sixty or so," Justin said.

Kit giggled. "Silly. Women can't have babies when they're sixty."

"You don't know *my* mother," Justin replied with a laugh.

They were both hungry, so Kit fixed them sandwiches, her favorite—salami and sprouts. Afterwards, she changed into a comfortable old pair of jeans and sweat shirt, and put on the new Lionel Richie album she'd bought last week with the money left over from her father's check.

"This is nice." Justin tucked an arm about her shoulders as she curled up next to him on the couch. "It's really comfortable, I mean. My dad goes in for the modern look. Lots of leather and chrome, that kind of thing. It can get depressing after a while. You feel like you're in a dentist's office waiting to get your teeth filled."

Kit followed his gaze about the living room, seeing it for the first time through Justin's eyes. Lit by the buttery glow of a pair of lamps Janice had had made from thick pewter candlesticks, it had the soft sepia look of an old photograph. She felt a new appreciation for her mother, who had made the most of their cramped, run-down apartment by painting the walls a delicate egg-shell and covering the worn spots in the carpet with colorful throw rugs. Grandma's old cheval-glass mirror stood in one corner, beside a copper jug stuffed with dried flowers. Kit could see their reflections in the wavy glass; she and Justin looked as if they were floating underwater.

Justin leaned close, his breath a flutter of warmth against her cheek. Then he was kissing her lightly on the mouth. She could feel the tip of his tongue, soft and searching. Kit still had that same floaty, underwater feeling from before, only it was as if someone had dropped a stone into the pool, sending ripple after ripple of sensation washing over her. She'd never been kissed like this before . . .

Justin's arms tightened about her. He was trembling slightly. Did he feel the same way?

Kit found herself responding to his deepening kisses in a way she never would have dreamed possible. She didn't panic when she felt the warm pressure of Justin's hand against her bare skin where her sweat shirt had pulled away from her jeans.

It felt nice.

His palm moved in slow circles against her stomach. His hand was smooth and gentle, not sweaty and demanding the way Derek's had been. She didn't mind when the circles widened, pushing higher and higher underneath her sweat shirt.

It felt good . . . so good . . . Justin touching her there . . . and there . . . and . . .

A soft insistent scratching sound grazed the edge of Kit's drifting consciousness. The record had ended, she realized. Someone had to lift the needle up. Gradually, she became aware of other things as well—the quick way she and Justin were breathing; the nubby fabric of the couch pressing into her back; the room's sudden suffocating closeness.

She looked up and caught a glimpse of herself in the mirror. This time, there was nothing dreamy about the way she looked. She lay sprawled on the couch with her sweat shirt bunched up and her hair sticking out every which way. Her lipstick was smeared about her mouth in a pink blur. Kit flushed with embarrassment. She sat up abruptly, yanking her sweat shirt down.

"I'd better change the record. Do you like the Eagles? I have the whole collection. If you like Fleetwood Mac, I have everything of theirs, too." She knew she was rattling on like an idiot, but she was unable to stop. "I guess I sort of go crazy when I like a group. My mother does, too. She has every record the Beatles have ever made. Do you like—"

Justin silenced her with a kiss. "You don't have to get up," he murmured huskily. "I like it when it's quiet, too."

Kit tried to relax as he went on kissing her, but all the good feelings had vanished. She didn't know why—only that she was scared now and wanted him to stop.

Obviously, Justin didn't feel the same way. His face was flushed, with a sleepy-eyed expression.

"Kit." He spoke her name softly. Kit felt her stomach tighten.

Justin, I'm sorry, I—no, please, I can't."

She tried to untangle herself from his embrace, but Justin only drew her closer.

"Don't worry, Kit. I won't hurt you."

Kit stiffened instantly. I've heard that one before, she thought. Was he telling her they should do It? Last summer she'd dated a boy who was always trying to get her to do It. Finally he stopped trying to convince her, and tried forcing her, instead. Kit remembered with horror how he'd tugged and pulled at her clothes while murmuring, "I'm not going to hurt you, Kit. I promise. It won't hurt a bit. You'll like it . . ."

Panic welled up in her at the memory. Fortunately, nothing had happened. She'd managed to escape unscathed, but she would never forget the experience.

Kit hardly knew what she was doing as she pushed Justin away. She struggled awkwardly to her feet and stood with her back to him, willing herself to stop shivering. Tears gathered in her throat.

She didn't want to cry. Crying was for other things. Right now, she wasn't sad. She was angry—angry at Justin for trying to force her into doing It. For taking a fragile, beautiful thing and shattering it with a single careless sentence. She was angry at herself, too, for letting herself trust a boy as much as she'd trusted Justin. And for liking him—maybe even loving him—when it was clear he'd only been interested in her for one thing. All that talk about wanting to get to know her—she should've known it was just a line!

"Kit?" She felt Justin's hand on her shoulder, light and questioning. "What's wrong? Look at me. Please."

"Nothing's wrong!" she choked. She couldn't face him. She didn't want him to see the tears that were starting to run down her cheeks. "I'm just tired, that's all. You'd better go home."

Justin tried to draw her into his arms, but she went rigid, her whole body freezing in defense. She forced her voice past the ache in her throat.

"*Just . . . go . . . home.*"

She turned around. Justin's face was a wobbly blur. All she could see was the hurt expression, the astonished gape of his mouth. In that instant, she suddenly wanted to erase that look, to put everything back the way it was.

No, that was crazy. It was Justin's fault, not hers. He was the one who had ruined it all.

Justin didn't say a word. He just turned and walked out. The door gave a soft, sorry little click as he shut it behind him. He was gone. With a cry, Kit crumpled onto the couch, burying her face in the cushions as she gave in to her sobs.

She wasn't aware of the door opening, and then closing again a few minutes later as her mother entered the apartment. Then Janice was bending over her with a little puff of perfumed air. She wrapped an arm around Kit's shoulders.

"Kit, honey, what *is* it?"

Kit longed to tell her everything, but the words just wouldn't come. Janice wouldn't understand.

She hardly understood what had happened herself. Suddenly, Kit realized she wasn't mad at Justin anymore. She was mad at herself.

Why am I such a freak? she wondered. Her mother would probably tell her not to worry, it was something she would grow out of, but Kit wasn't so sure. Maybe she'd stay a virgin for the rest of her life. She'd once read a story in *Modern Romances* about a woman who got married and couldn't do It with her own husband. Finally, the man got so disgusted with her, he divorced her and she ended up marrying her psychiatrist.

Why did sex have to be such a big deal? *Lots* of people did It. Even people you never would have suspected—like old Mrs. Lanitsky, who had pictures of her grandchildren all over her walls to prove it. Then there was Cornelia Waverley, the fat girl in her English class last year, who turned out to be fat for a reason. And what about her own mother, for goodness' sake?

In the fourth grade, when she, Elaine and Alex first found out about sex, they'd discussed it with the kind of skepticism formerly reserved for things like ghosts and UFOs. Alex refused to believe *her* parents had ever done such a disgusting thing, even after Elaine had logically pointed out that she herself was walking proof that they had. Finally, Alex was forced to admit they had probably done It but insisted it had only happened twice. Once for herself and once for her brother. Beyond that, she wouldn't budge. As Kit remembered it, she and Elaine hadn't pressed too hard. They were having a tough time as it was believing the awful truth about *their* parents.

When did it all change? Kit wondered. When had the prospect of getting kissed gone from being rated below black jelly beans to practically the most important thing on earth? Look at Alex. Even she was thinking of doing It.

No, Kit decided. She couldn't tell her mother what had happened tonight . . . or rather, what *hadn't* happened. Mom wouldn't understand. To her, sex was natural. Like breathing. Only to Kit, it was like trying to breathe underwater. Every time she tried, she felt as if she were drowning.

Chapter Nine

"Maybe it's like skiing or surfing," Elaine suggested hopefully. "You have to fall down a lot before you get to like it."

Kit trudged beside her on their way to gym class, feeling gloomier with each step. She knew Elaine was only trying to cheer her up, but she'd already decided that nothing could cheer her up. This week had probably been the worst week of her entire life, and it wasn't over yet.

Today was Thursday. She and Justin hadn't spoken to each other since the night of the prom—except, of course, at work when they absolutely had to. As if that wasn't bad enough, she'd been so upset yesterday, she'd blown her audition for the Summer Dance Repertory Theater. And she'd been practically counting on getting that position for the summer.

Kit sighed. "It doesn't matter how I feel about it

anymore. Justin and I aren't even on speaking terms, so what difference does it make? It's over."

"Have you *tried* talking to him? You can't know anything for sure until you've at least tried. Remember the time I was so worried about gymnastics tryouts? I was sure I'd fall flat on my face. You told me that nothing ever turns out to be as bad as you imagine it to be. And you were right."

"I take it back. In this case, it's probably worse."

"Come on, Kit. You don't know that for sure. What do you have to lose? The worst he can do is ignore you, and he's already doing that." Elaine bit her lip. "Gosh, there I go putting my foot in my mouth again. I'm sorry, Kit. I guess it's not so easy giving advice on a subject you know zilch about."

Kit grabbed the opportunity to change the subject. "What do you mean? I saw you talking to a boy at your locker just a few minutes ago. Wasn't he the same one you were dancing with at the prom?"

Elaine blushed scarlet. "Oh, you mean Rusty Hughes. He was just looking for someone to tutor him. His father wants him to bone up on his math before the SATs—just in case he doesn't get a football scholarship to college. That's why Rusty asked me to dance at Homecoming. He wanted to know if I'd be interested."

It was plain to Kit that there was more to it than that, at least as far as Elaine was concerned, but she didn't press the subject. Poor Elaine looked pretty uncomfortable about the whole thing. She was probably crazy about Rusty, and he was ignoring her from the neck down. In her own case, Kit reflected, it was just the opposite.

They'd taken the shortcut across the soccer field, forgetting that it was still wet from yesterday's rain. By the time she reached the girls' locker room, Kit's sneakers were soaked. She squelched her way down the aisle toward her locker, leaving a trail of waffled prints in her wake.

Following behind her, Elaine made one last stab at trying to convince her to talk to Justin. "Kit, think of it this way. It couldn't hurt . . . and it might even help. Maybe he's just as confused about this whole thing as you are."

"I . . . I wish I *could* talk to him," Kit admitted, staring at her wet sneakers lethargically. "I have a feeling it wouldn't do any good, though. Elaine, you weren't *there*. You didn't see the way I acted."

"What exactly *did* happen?" Elaine asked.

"I'm not even sure myself. It felt good . . . at first. Then, I don't know, suddenly I got scared and it didn't feel so good anymore. I just freaked out. I . . . I got mad at Justin and told him to leave. Why *wouldn't* he be disgusted with me after all that?"

"You should try explaining how you felt to him," Elaine said. "Even if he is disgusted with you, I don't see how he could stay that way once he knows why you blew up."

"Even *I* don't know why I freaked out," Kit

groaned. "Maybe it's because I'm so inexperienced. Or maybe I'm just weird that way. Anyway, if I knew the answer, I wouldn't be in this mess." She turned to Elaine. "Why did I have to make such a big deal out of it?"

Elaine blinked thoughtfully behind her big tortoiseshell glasses. "It *is* a big deal, Kit. At least, I know it will be for me. The trouble is, everybody tries to act so nonchalant about it. Take those ads, for instance, where the woman calls the guy up and invites him over for a drink. Like if you keep a certain kind of liquor in your cupboard, that's all it takes. Or a pair of designer jeans, or whatever. But I'll bet there're a lot of people who feel the way you do. When you get right down to it, if sex was no big deal, why would everyone spend so much time talking about it?"

"Well, I'm tired of talking about it," Kit responded angrily. "Maybe it's time I—" she was cut off by the deafening jangle of the second bell.

She'd been about to say that maybe it was about time she stopped being so inexperienced. It was a wild thought, but this wasn't the first time it had crept into her mind. It was the first time she'd felt desperate enough to consider it seriously though. It was a little like being afraid of the dark, Kit reflected. When she was younger, she used to lie awake at night after her mother turned out the lights, conjuring up all sorts of ghostly shapes and lurking monsters. Sometimes when it got really bad she would cry for Janice, but when the lights were switched on again, she could see that the monster crouching in the corner was just her dresser, and the ghost was only the curtains blowing in the breeze.

Maybe she was afraid of sex only because she didn't know what it was all about. Maybe if she understood what was involved, she'd be less fearful . . .

Elaine grabbed Kit's sleeve. "We'd better hurry. We have exactly one second to get into our gym suits."

Kit groaned. "I just remembered. I left mine in my other locker. God, this'll be my third tardy slip this week. Mrs. Gonzalez is going to kill me!"

"At least you're not as bad as Stephanie Bryce," Elaine pointed out. "She's always trying to get out of swimming. It drives Mrs. Gonzalez crazy. Stephanie's the only girl I know who has three periods a month."

Kit was charging across the quad when she spotted a familiar figure in the distance ahead. Her heart leaped into her throat at the sight of Justin's quick, purposeful stride. Abruptly, she slowed, looking desperately about for a way to escape before he saw her—but it was too late. She was the only other person around. He couldn't miss her if he tried.

Heat flooded Kit's cheeks in a painful rush as Justin approached. Maybe Elaine was right, she thought. Maybe she should try to talk to him . . . to somehow explain. Perhaps he didn't really hate her as much as she'd imagined . . .

"Hi," she squeaked, managing to unstick her

voice only after she'd swallowed several times.

"Hi," he said cautiously. He slowed, but didn't stop, as if he were waiting for her to make the first move.

Kit struggled desperately to think of something to say—something warm and brilliant and disarming that would erase the memory of the past five days. But all she could come up with was the kind of dumb remark people always make when they're trying too hard to be warm and brilliant.

"Looks like we're late," she mumbled.

Justin shoved back a windblown curl that corkscrewed down over one eye. "Yeah. Looks that way."

"I forgot my gym suit," she explained.

"I got hung up at a student council meeting."

Kit pasted a stiff smile in place. "Well . . . I guess I'd better hurry."

"Me too."

"Bye."

"Seeya."

Kit fought the urge to run after him. It was no use. She'd been right after all. He didn't want to have anything to do with her. It was obvious, wasn't it? He'd acted as if they were practically strangers! Kit found her way to her locker, so depressed she could hardly see straight. She had to turn the lock several times before she got the combination right.

One thought pounded through her brain. *If only I hadn't blown it that night. If only I hadn't acted like such a dope. If only . . .*

"It's always easy until you get to the windmill." Alex positioned her golf club in front of the ball. "That's where they get you every time."

Kit watched in admiration as Alex whacked the ball in a straight line that carried it through the windmill, over the bridge, and down the short carpeted hill and into the cup.

"If that's your idea of blowing it, I'm not sure I even want to try," Lori remarked. "Next time you want someone to play miniature golf with, try calling up Arnold Palmer."

"I tried, but his line was busy," Alex joked, her brown eyes dancing. "So I'm stuck with you two instead. Anyway, I'm not all that crazy about miniature golf. I just thought Kit could use some cheering up."

Kit forced a smile. She hadn't really wanted to come in the first place, but when Alex called, she was so intent on cheering her up, Kit didn't have the heart to say no. Only Elaine was absent. She was home, sweating over her Stanford interview, which was tomorrow. According to Elaine, she already had three strikes against her: 1. She was nervous, 2. She always sweated when she was nervous, 3. There wasn't enough deodorant in the whole world to keep her from sweating through her blouse.

"Maybe you should've called Ann Landers instead," Kit said. "I tried taking Elaine's advice, and look where it got me. Exactly nowhere."

Alex and Lori exchanged looks. Kit had already

filled them in on the whole story about Justin's brush-off.

"Are you sure you tried hard enough?" Lori asked gently.

"Sure," Alex put in. "There's talking and there's *talking*. Did you tell Justin how you really feel?"

"He never gives me a chance. He practically runs away every time he sees me. The only time he can't run away is at work. But how much romance is there in telling someone to hold the mushrooms on a large pepperoni?"

"He might be as frustrated as you are," Lori suggested. "He probably wants to talk to you, too—only he can't get up the nerve."

Kit shook her head. "You haven't seen the way he looks at me." She bit her lip. "Like . . . like I'm not even there. Like I could be living in Mongolia or something and he wouldn't know the difference!"

It was Kit's turn to take a swing. Alex handed her the club she was carrying. "Here, maybe its luck will rub off on you."

Kit swung half-heartedly, watching as the ball dribbled a few feet then sank into the pond with a dismal plop. She dropped down on the nearby bench, feeling more miserable than ever.

"See? It's hopeless. I can't do anything right. I can't kiss a boy without freaking out. I can't even score one crummy point in miniature golf!"

"I don't think you can really compare the two," Alex said. "But I know how you feel. Once, Danny and I had this huge fight and didn't speak to each other for a whole week. I was so depressed, then I decided, this is ridiculous—we have to talk."

Lori groaned. "I remember. That was the night you came over to my house and we ate our way through an entire half gallon of fudge swirl ice cream. I gained two pounds!"

"I always eat when I'm depressed," Alex explained. "Besides I was just trying to work up the courage to phone Danny. I must have dialed him and hung up at least fifty times before I finally let it ring. Only it didn't ring. I got a busy signal instead. In fact the phone was busy for so long, I thought Danny might be talking to another girl. When I finally got through, I was so mad I was ready to tell him off all over again. But as it turned out, the phone had been busy because *he'd* been dialing *my* number all night."

Despite her misery, Kit found herself laughing with Alex and Lori. "I remember now. I was trying to call Lori that night. You were on the phone for three hours!"

"We had a lot of talking to make up for," Alex said with a sheepish expression. "But don't you see, Kit? The point is, we *did* talk. We got it all out in the open."

The only thing Kit saw was that it had worked for Alex and Danny. But it was different for them. They were going steady, for one thing. She and Justin were just getting to know each other.

Now it looked as though they were never going to get the chance.

"What's the use of talking to him, anyway?" she sighed. "Even if we did get back together, I'd probably do the same thing again next time he tried to kiss me. I might as well face it—I'm never going to get anywhere with Justin until I'm more . . . well, *experienced*."

Lori's eyebrows shot up in alarm. "What are you talking about? You're not thinking of—Kit, you wouldn't!"

"I don't know," Kit said. "I just don't know."

She'd been giving it a lot of thought these past few days. Maybe that was her only hope—finding someone who would give her the experience she needed.

Kit was in the bathroom, brushing her teeth before bed, when the phone rang. Justin? She nearly swallowed a mouthful of toothpaste as she choked out "I'll get it!" to her mother. Her hand trembled as she picked up the receiver.

But it wasn't Justin.

"Kit? Is that you?" her father asked.

"Of course, it's me, Daddy! Who did you think?"

"Sorry, Kitten. You sounded like your mother just then."

Kit wasn't sure he'd meant it as a compliment, knowing the way he felt about Janice, but she decided not to let it bother her. She was so happy to hear from him.

He chuckled. "Don't tell me you went and grew up behind my back?"

"Oh, Daddy." Kit was torn between a giggle and a sigh of exasperation. Her father probably would always think of her as a baby—he'd called her Kitten ever since she could remember.

They talked about school, her grade-point average, which colleges she was applying to. He told her about the vacation he and Vi had taken to Palm Springs last month. Finally, he coughed—a signal that meant he was getting to the real reason for the call.

"I'm flying up from L.A. in a few weeks," he told her. "Company business. I'll only be in town for the day, but I thought it'd be nice if you and I could get together for dinner. There's something I'd like to talk to you about."

Kit felt a pang of uneasiness. She hoped it wasn't bad news. The last time he'd wanted to talk to her alone had been to tell her that he and Janice were getting a divorce. What could it be this time?

"I'd like that," she said, keeping her voice as even as possible.

There was a short silence on the other end, then her father said, "I miss you, Kitten, you know that."

Kit was too choked up to answer. Instead of telling him how much she missed him, too, she thanked him again for the money he'd sent. They promised to write more, and he said he would call her when he got to the airport.

She hung up feeling sad. Except for these scattered phone calls and visits, and the two weeks she spent with them in the summer, she really wasn't a part of her father's life anymore.

On impulse, Kit picked up the phone again, quickly dialing Justin's number before she could talk herself out of it. What her friends had said tonight made sense. She *hadn't* tried hard enough to talk to Justin this afternoon. She'd been caught off-guard when she saw him, unable to think of anything even remotely intelligent to say. This time it would be different.

Kit listened to the phone ring. Three times. Four. Her palm was starting to sweat. She had to squeeze hard to keep the receiver from slipping out of her hand. Finally, someone picked it up.

"Hello?" It was a girl's voice.

Kit's stomach did a sick jellyfish flop. Her throat closed around her voice like a fist. Justin didn't have any sisters; he and his father lived alone. What would a girl be doing over at his house unless . . .

If the girl on the other end of the phone was Justin's date, Kit didn't want to know. Not knowing wasn't as terrible as finding out that what she suspected was true.

"Who *is* this?" The girl sounded a little impatient.

Kit slammed the phone down, her heart banging painfully against her ribs. On knees that had suddenly turned to water, she stumbled back into her bedroom, crawling into bed the way she had as a child when she was really upset about something—knees tucked against her chest, the covers pulled up to her chin. She was shivering, even though she wasn't cold.

Kit closed her eyes, but couldn't get rid of the picture that was pasted behind her eyelids—the picture of Justin sitting on his couch, his arm curled around the girl at his side. They were kissing.

It was a long time before she could get to sleep.

Chapter Ten

"You creep! I'll get you for that!"

Kit could hear Alex's screeches at the other end of the parking lot, where she was busy sudsing down a sky-blue Cadillac. Alex and Danny were at it again with their hoses. In the past hour, since the launching of the Senior Car Wash, they'd probably managed to spray more water on each other than on the cars.

Earlier, Kit had counted more than two dozen seniors strung out across the shopping center lot with their buckets and hoses. It was a warm, sunny day, so there was no shortage of customers. They were working in groups of two and three; Kit and Lori had paired off at one end, Danny and Alex at the other.

Kit glanced up just as Alex flung a soapy sponge at Danny, her face alight with mischief. It caught him on the shoulder, spraying flecks of foam up the side of his face. In retaliation, he took aim with his hose, but missed her when she ducked behind a Chevy van.

"There's no escape!" he yelled. "It won't do you any good to beg for mercy, either."

Alex popped up indignantly. "Since when have I ever begged?"

Danny took advantage of the moment to blast her with his hose. Afterwards, while she stood there dripping, he laughed, "I knew that would get you."

Kit's heart constricted in envy. They were having so much fun. A lot of the other couples were clowning around, too. She heard Marcia Connors squeal as Derek Johnson stuck his hose down the back of her T-shirt. Kit had heard they were dating, and from the way they were acting, she could believe it.

She found herself thinking about Justin. She was positive now he was never going to make a move. It had been exactly two weeks since their fight—if you could call it that—and nothing had changed. At school they continued to ignore each other; at work, they acted like two strangers forced to speak to each other out of politeness. Had they ever really been more than strangers?

"Hey, you're supposed to be washing the car off, not my foot!"

Kit was jerked out of her daydreams by Lori's good-natured complaint. She gave Lori an apologetic shrug. "Sorry. Guess I was thinking about something else."

"Justin?"

Kit nodded.

Lori winced in sympathy. "Oh, Kit, I wish there was something I could do to help. I hate seeing you this way."

"I'll get over it, I suppose." *In about a hundred years*, she thought. Then with more spirit than she felt, she added, "Justin's not the only boy in the world, you know."

"Sure. I can think of a few others," Lori replied with a rueful expression.

Lori looked fabulous, Kit thought—even with her hair hanging in wet strands and not a speck of makeup. She was wearing a pair of khaki shorts and a midriff top that showed off her tiny waist.

"Is Ben still calling?" Kit asked. Poor Ben Price had been hopelessly infatuated with Lori ever since their prom date. Unfortunately, the feeling wasn't mutual. Lori was having a hard time getting the message through to him.

Lori flushed. "He called again last night. Honestly, Kit, I'm running out of excuses. I've already used the baby-sitting line three times. This time, I told him I was going to my cousin Shirley's wedding. I don't even *have* a cousin named Shirley, much less one who's getting married."

"Why don't you tell him the truth—that you're just not interested?"

"I couldn't do *that*." Lori looked horrified at the suggestion.

Kit knew that Lori hated to hurt anyone's feelings, but sometimes she thought Lori took it a little too far. "Look at the situation honestly," she said, plunging her sponge into the bucket. "You're not doing his ego any favors this way, either. Sooner or later, he's going to figure it out."

"I know, I know," Lori groaned. "I just wish I didn't have to be the one to tell him."

"Maybe you could say you have a steady boyfriend. Someone who doesn't go to Glenwood. Make him a black belt in karate while you're at it."

"Oh, Kit, you're too much!" Lori giggled, and went back to rinsing off her side of the car.

Kit was wiping off the windshield when a low-slung silver Porsche purred to a stop at her station. A dark-haired boy wearing reflector sunglasses stuck his head out the window.

"Do you do this kind of thing for a living or just for kicks?" he asked.

His voice sounded vaguely familiar. Kit shaded her eyes against the bright sunlight to get a better look.

"It's for a good cause," she said. "We're raising money for our senior picnic. Need a wash?"

"Best invitation I've had all day."

He grinned, pushing his sunglasses on top of his head. His eyes were a very pale blue. She wasn't sure whether it was the lightness of his eyes or the fact that he was staring at her that made her so nervous. Suddenly, she felt terribly conscious of her cutoffs, and the way her wet

T-shirt was clinging to her.

"You know, you really look a lot like your mother," he said. "She's a real knockout."

Suddenly, Kit remembered where she'd met him. His father owned the company where Janice worked. Kit had met him once, when she picked her mother up at her office. His name was Rich Garrison. She knew very little about him, except that he was older than she was and that he raced cars for a hobby.

"Thanks," Kit mumbled, not knowing what else to say. She started toward the car just as he opened the door to step out, and tripped over the hose that was tangled at her feet.

Rich grabbed her just before she fell. It seemed to her his hands lingered on her ribcage several seconds longer than necessary. Flustered, she drew away.

"Are you always this graceful?" Rich laughed.

Kit gulped, too embarrassed for words. Finally, she blurted. "Do you want it waxed, too? It's five dollars extra."

"What?"

"Your car."

"Oh that. Never mind about the car. I'm in a hurry." He pulled out his wallet and handed her a crisp five-dollar bill. "But since it's for a good cause, here, take the money anyway."

Kit shook her head. "Oh no, I can't—it wouldn't be right. I didn't do anything."

Rich gave her a long look full of teasing invitation. She decided he was handsome—in an arrogant kind of way—not really her type, but definitely worth a second look.

"Actually," he said, "There *is* something you can do for me. How about giving me your phone number?"

"What for?" Kit asked, feeling stupid the instant she said it.

Rich smiled. "You don't have a boyfriend, do you?"

Kit thought about Justin for a moment, feeling a pang of emptiness as she answered "No."

"Good. Then there shouldn't be any problem."

Still, Kit hesitated. Rich was so sure of himself. *Too* sure. But maybe that was just what she needed. An older man—someone with a lot of experience. Rich was at least twenty-five, she guessed. He'd probably been to bed with lots of women. So what if he wasn't her type? Everything had changed since she'd lost Justin. She was desperate now.

Kit scribbled her number on the piece of paper he handed her—quickly, before she could change her mind.

"I don't believe it." Elaine stared at Kit in horror. "An older guy invites you up to his parents' cabin in the mountains and you said *yes*. Kit, have you gone completely bananas?"

Kit ducked her head, rummaging in her locker so Elaine wouldn't see the way her cheeks were burning. She didn't feel nearly as sure about this whole thing as she wanted Elaine to think.

"I don't see what's so terrible about it," Kit said in defense. "Anyway, he said it was going to be a party."

Kit had told her about Rich's phone call as they rode their bikes to school Monday morning. Now inside the school building, she braced herself for her friend's reaction. Elaine was wearing a green corduroy jumper over her favorite yellow striped sweater. Her hair was pulled back in a ponytail, making her cheekbones, which were flushed both from the ride and her indignation over Kit's news, stand out more than ever.

"What about *after* the party?" she wanted to know. "You know what those older guys are like. They *expect* it. Carol Morgenstern told me she went to a fraternity party once where everybody got drunk. This guy took her to his room, and when she wanted to leave, he wouldn't let her."

Kit felt a little pull in her stomach. "What happened?"

"What do you *think* happened?"

Kit didn't want to think about it. She clenched her jaw stubbornly as she fished her Chemistry book from the depths of her locker.

"It's not going to be like that," she said.

"Come on, Kit—even *I'm* not that dumb!" Elaine cried in exasperation.

Kit looked up at her. "Okay, so what if he does try something? Maybe it wouldn't be the worst thing in the world. Maybe I'm tired of . . . of being a freak! Maybe a night with Rich Garrison is just what I need!"

Elaine blinked at her. "What are you yelling for?"

"Who's yelling!"

Elaine laid a sympathetic hand against her shoulder. "Kit, I know how it is. I feel like a freak, too, sometimes. I mean, look at this thing with Rusty. To him, I'm just a walking brain. Sometimes, I wonder what would happen if I just—" she stopped, a blush rising from the high neck of her sweater. "Oh well, you get the point. I guess what I'm trying to say is, *feeling* a certain way about something doesn't always mean you have to *do* anything about it."

Kit shook her head. "You don't understand. Unless I *do* something, I'll never have a chance at getting Justin to like me."

"I think," Elaine said in a slow, thoughtful voice, "what's more important is liking yourself."

Elaine's words gnawed at Kit throughout the next two periods. In Chemistry, she could barely concentrate on the experiment she was supposed to be doing, and had to wash the whole thing down the sink in the end. Then Miss Kramer, her History teacher, sprang a multiple-choice quiz on Important Battles of World War II. Kit could only stare blankly at the questions. How could she be expected to remember the date Rommel invaded Egypt when her own life was such a mess?

In spite of her brave words to Elaine, Kit was more than a little scared about going out with Rich. What if she was right? What if it turned out to be the biggest mistake of her life?

108

Then Kit reminded herself that she hadn't done anything yet. It was just a date, right? And Rich Garrison was a perfectly nice person—not Dracula.

Alex, in her own inimitable fashion, gave Kit her opinion while the four of them were eating lunch in the cafeteria.

"It's like going out with King Kong, just to get to the top of the Empire State Building," she said, chomping down on a carrot stick. "What's the point—unless you happen to be in love with King Kong?"

"You make it sound so awful," Kit said. "It's only a party."

"At an isolated cabin in the woods," Elaine interjected.

"With a guy you hardly know," Lori chimed in, twirling the ends of her silky blond hair as she sipped her milk. "Kit, I *saw* the way he was looking at you at the car wash. I thought I was going to have to spray him with my hose to cool him off."

Out of the corner of her eye, Kit caught sight of Justin as he was rounding the end of their table, balancing a loaded tray in each hand. Roseanne Parker, a petite red-haired cheerleader, walked beside him. Justin had his head bent to one side to hear what she was saying. Kit felt sick. She didn't realize she was staring until their eyes met. One corner of his mouth turned up in a half-smile of greeting. Kit quickly looked away, pretending to be absorbed in what was on her tray.

Was Justin dating her? Was it Roseanne who had answered the phone that night when she called? An image of Justin kissing Roseanne flashed through her mind, making Kit feel even sicker.

"Kit—you don't look too good." Lori was peering at her with a concerned expression.

"Lunch had the same effect on me," Alex said. "Did anyone figure out what it was?"

"Meatloaf—I think," Elaine said doubtfully, stabbing at the remains on her plate with a fork. "Or maybe chili. Someone should do an autopsy."

Kit giggled in spite of herself. "My whole life is in ruins, and you're talking about dead meatloaf! I think I'm going to be sick."

Alex slipped a tanned arm about her shoulders. "I'm sorry. I know what it's like to break up with someone you really care about."

"Sure," Lori kidded her. "That's because you and Danny have broken up about a hundred and eighty times." When she turned to Kit, her blue eyes were full of sympathy. "We just don't want to see you get hurt even worse, Kit."

How could she be hurt any worse? Kit wondered.

"If I don't go, I'm doomed," she said.

"You could be doomed if you do," Elaine warned.

Kit sighed, shoving her untouched tray aside. "I guess it's a chance I'll have to take."

110

Chapter Eleven

"Absolutely not. It's out of the question, Kit."

Kit couldn't believe what she was hearing. She stared at her mother. Janice's mouth was compressed in a tight line, her eyes an unrelenting blue. Kit had never seen her mom act this way. The heavy mother bit just wasn't Janice.

Kit was perched on a stool at the kitchen counter, watching her mother make a salad. Janice tore off a lettuce leaf and tossed it into the bowl. She wore a man's shirt—one Kit had never seen before—which was untucked and hung down almost to the knees of her Levi's. Her feet were bare.

"For one thing, he's too old for you," Janice went on. "And for another, he's too—well, there's been some talk at work. I won't go into it all, but let's just say he's not Mr. Clean as far as reputations go."

Kit frowned as she picked at a tomato seed that had dried and stuck to the counter. "I don't care if he isn't Mr. Clean," she said.

"Well, *I* care, even if you don't. I am your mother, after all, even if we both need to remind ourselves of that fact once in a while." She looked at Kit, her mouth relaxing. "Kit, you're too sensible not to see what's going on. Why do you think a boy like Rich would be interested in a seventeen-year-old girl?"

"Sex," she tossed back off-handedly, "What else?" She'd wanted to shock her mother, but Kit felt shocked herself. What had made her say *that*?

Janice stopped in the middle of slicing a green onion. She stared at Kit. "I don't believe I'm hearing this from you."

Kit rose from her stool in a flush of anger. "Why not? Aren't you the one who's always telling me how natural it is?"

"Kit, there's a time and a place . . ." Janice trailed off uncertainly. She wore a slightly bewildered expression, like a driver who's not sure which way to turn next. Finally, she gave a deep sigh and scooped back a handful of her honey-blond hair with one damp hand. "Sex is only natural and good between two people who care about each other," she finished quietly.

"Does that mean you're in love with Doug?" Kit demanded.

"I don't know. Maybe. Anyway, that's not the p—"

"What *is* the point then?" Tears of outrage pricked at Kit's eyes. "If it's okay for *you* to sleep with whoever you want, why should it be different for me?"

Janice winced. Bright spots of color formed high on her cheekbones. "I'm older, for one thing. I'm careful, too. You have to be careful about feelings, Kit. You aren't the only one who can get hurt. I know, believe me."

"Why should I believe you? You lied to me about Hugh."

Kit hadn't even realized she was angry about Hugh until she said it. Hugh was Janice's first steady boyfriend after the divorce. He even lived with them for a few months. Kit had liked Hugh. He was a tall man who walked with a slight stoop, as if he were used to ducking under doorways. He had gentle eyes and a bushy reddish beard. In the evenings, they sometimes played chess. Then one afternoon, Kit had come home from school to find that Hugh's steel-stringed Martin guitar wasn't propped in its usual place behind the sofa. She checked the closets, discovering that he'd moved the rest of his things out, too.

"I never lied about Hugh," Janice told her.

"You said you were going to marry him."

"I thought so for a while. Until things changed."

"I'll bet you never loved Daddy, either," Kit tossed at her.

Janice went back to chopping onions. Her mouth had gone tight again, and the red spots on

113

her cheeks had spread. "Your father and I—well, it was such a long time ago. Let's just forget it, okay?"

Kit's tears spilled over in a hot rush. "I *can't*. Maybe he's not your husband anymore, but he's still my father!"

"Oh, Kit." Janice looked as if she were going to cry, too. "I didn't mean it that way. God, I'm making a mess of this whole thing, aren't I? Look, can't we talk about it some other time? Doug'll be here any minute and I'm not even dressed."

Choked with rage, Kit fled from the kitchen. She heard the clatter of a knife, and Janice called out, "Kit!" but her only response was to slam her bedroom door with all the strength she could muster.

"Hey, are you okay?" Rich asked. "You seem kind of quiet."

"I guess I just don't feel much like talking," Kit told him.

It had been two days since the blow-up with her mother, and even though Kit hadn't gotten over her resentment, she couldn't help feeling guilty about sneaking out behind Janice's back. No matter how many times she told herself that Janice was being unreasonable, and that she wasn't really doing anything wrong, she still felt bad. What made it even worse was that she'd told her mother she was spending the night with Alex. Now Alex was involved in the lie, too, and even though she'd agreed to cover for Kit, she wasn't happy about it.

Rich smiled. "Hey, no problem. I know what you mean. I like a little peace and quiet myself sometimes. That's why I thought it'd be more fun this way."

With an expert twist of the steering wheel, he guided the Porsche off the steep mountain drive they'd been climbing and onto a narrower dirt road. His headlights cut a swath of green through the densely wooded darkness.

"What way?" Kit asked, feeling nervous. Her palms were starting to sweat. She wiped them along the sides of her jeans.

"Just the two of us," he said, flashing her The Look.

The level of Kit's unease rose a notch. "I thought you said it was going to be a party."

"Sure, but who needs big parties? It's better like this; we'll make our own party—more intimate, you know what I mean?" He glanced over at her again. "Hey, you seem kind of jumpy. You're not one of those girls who turns into a pumpkin at midnight, are you?"

"Who, me?" Kit forced a smile. She was thinking about Justin. If only he were with her instead!

The Garrisons' cabin was at the end of a winding dead-end road. She couldn't see much of the outside, because it was so dark, but the inside was very modern-looking, with lots of redwood panelling and exposed beams. There was a fireplace in the middle of the living room, but even so, Kit couldn't imagine it ever being a warm place. She shivered. Rich slipped an arm about her shoulders.

"Cold? I'll get you a drink. That'll warm you up." He pulled out a bottle from one of the cabinets and poured an amber-colored liquid into two glasses.

Kit took a sip. Her eyes watered as the liquor burned its way down her throat. She managed a few more sips, then put it down. Her head was starting to feel as if it were packed in cotton.

Rich dropped down beside her on the sofa, drink in hand. "Nice, huh? My parents built it as a weekend house, but they hardly ever come up here, anymore. Most of the time, I have it all to myself. It's a great place to unwind after a race."

"Do you do a lot of racing?" she asked.

"I haven't gone pro yet, if that's what you mean, but yeah, I follow the amateur circuit pretty closely."

Kit noticed how carefully his hair was styled— you could almost see the tracks his comb had made. The strong scent of his aftershave mingled with the smell of whiskey. Why was he looking at her that way? She didn't know what to say. It was weird—like being in a movie, and not knowing what your next line was.

Rich put on some music, then sat down again, this time slinging an arm around her. Before she knew what was happening, he was kissing her. His mouth pushed her upper lip against her teeth as it mashed down on hers. Kit had to fight

116

the impulse to pull away. She told herself she was just nervous. It would get better once she relaxed. Even so, she couldn't help stiffening when Rich's hand crept up under her sweater and shirt, and began fumbling for the clasp on her bra.

"Damn," he muttered when he couldn't find it.

Hot with shame, she finally told him, "It snaps in front."

Rich stood up, pulling her with him. "Come on—we can take our clothes off upstairs." His face was flushed, and he was breathing hard.

Kit took a deep, shaky breath. This was it. She had two choices. She could go through with it, or she could make a fool of herself by running away again. Not that she cared what Rich thought—it was Justin she was thinking of.

The bedroom was a large upstairs loft with no furniture except a dresser and an enormous bed. Kit sat down on it and promptly fell backwards.

"I like making it on a waterbed, don't you?" Rich sank down beside her, hooking a knee about her leg. The bed sloshed around underneath them in what Kit thought was a very unsexy way.

"It's . . . uh . . . nice," she stammered. She wondered if she should tell him she'd never done it anywhere, much less on a waterbed.

Rich's lips moved against her neck as he murmured, "You're really beautiful, you know that?"

Kit was silent; she didn't know what to say.

"Hey," he looked up, "I mean it. One thing about me, I don't believe in feeding anyone a line.

Like I'm not going to say I love you, okay? Some girls want you to say it, even if you don't mean it, but I'm not into that."

"It's all right," Kit said. "I don't love you, either."

"Fantastic." He grinned at her as he sat up and began unbuckling his belt.

Kit was having a hard time breathing, and all the sloshing around was making her feel as if she had to go to the bathroom. She closed her eyes when he started to unbutton her blouse. Maybe this was where it started to feel good, she thought. She waited for the good feelings to happen, but there was nothing. She just felt cold.

Suddenly, she knew she couldn't go through with it. This was all wrong. She never should have come. She didn't even like Rich.

Kit struggled to a sitting position, which wasn't all that easy with all the jostling around that was going on. "I'm sorry," she gulped. "I can't. It's not you . . . I just—there's something I forgot to do at home. I have to get back."

Rich squeezed her shoulder. "It can wait, baby. We have more important things to do."

Kit resisted this time when he tried to pull her back down beside him. It would have been funny, she thought, if she hadn't been so scared. The bed was rolling wildly, tossing them about like a pair of corks. Kit had to stifle a hysterical giggle.

The next instant, she was close to tears. "I don't feel like it!" she finally blurted out. "I just *don't*, okay? I'm sorry about this whole thing. I

118

just want to go home." Her voice wobbled at the mention of home.

Rich stopped struggling, and fixed her with a cold flat glare. "Hey, don't get all worked up over it," he drawled, switching from high gear to a cruising speed in a blink of an eye. "I've never had to force anyone. Sure, I'll take you home. When *I'm* ready."

He stalked out of the room. A minute later, she could hear him pacing around downstairs, then the clink of a bottle hitting the side of a glass.

Kit bit her lip to keep from crying. She'd really made a mess of things this time. What if Rich decided not to take her home at all? There wasn't even a telephone in the cabin so she could phone someone.

She didn't know how long she waited for Rich to cool off before she finally ventured downstairs. It was so quiet, she felt a new surge of panic, fearing he'd left without her. Then a low, rumbling noise caught her ear.

Rich was stretched out on the couch, snoring drunkenly. Kit's heart sank.

Now she was really stuck.

Chapter Twelve

Kit woke to the sound of rain pelting the roof. For a minute, she thought she was in her own bed at home. She stretched, wondering groggily why she'd worn her shoes to bed. Then she remembered. With a tiny cry, she jerked upright.

She wasn't home—she was still stuck in the cabin with Rich! Kit glanced at her watch and moaned. This was Saturday, and it was past nine—she should have been at work by now! Oh God, Mr. Watkins was going to kill her. No, it was even worse. He was going to fire her.

Rich drove her home in frozen silence. His eyes were bloodshot, his jaw darkened with stubble. Kit couldn't believe she'd ever thought he was handsome. When he dropped her off in front of her apartment, she rushed inside without a backward glance.

Kit dashed up the stairs two at a time. She was

sick with worry. Maybe if she called her boss and explained . . . what? She couldn't think of an explanation convincing enough to keep him from letting her go. And without the job . . . well, she just might as well give up on her dream of ever becoming a professional dancer.

Oh, how had she ever gotten into this mess? Why hadn't she listened to her friends? They'd warned her it would turn out this way.

The phone was ringing as Kit walked in the door. Her mother must not be home, since no one was answering it.

She snatched up the receiver. "Hello?"

"Kit? Is that you? Are you okay?" The sound of Justin's voice came as a warm, welcome shock. "You sound like you're out of breath."

"I ran all the way up."

His voice dropped to a whisper. "Listen, I can't talk. Mr. Watkins'll be back any minute. I told him you were sick. Kit, what happened? I was really worried. I've been trying all morning to call you."

Kit felt dazed with happiness. He was worried about her! He even covered for her with Mr. Watkins. She could hardly believe it. Did that mean he still cared about her?

"Temporary insanity," she muttered, remembering a phrase Elaine had once used.

"What?"

"Never mind. It's a long story. I'll tell you about it later." She paused. Her heart was in her throat as she asked, "Are you still coming to the show?

It's tonight, in case you forgot."

Justin didn't hesitate. "I wouldn't miss it!"

"I'm so nervous, I could die." Lori groaned. "My stomach is a mass of butterflies!"

"Don't worry," Alex laughed. "Butterflies aren't deadly as far as I know."

"I just hope our act doesn't kill the audience," Elaine said.

Kit tried to keep a straight face while she finished gluing on her mustache. Then she stood back and surveyed her reflection in the mirror that someone had propped up near the fire exit. She smiled. In a pin-striped man's suit, with her hair tucked up under a straw boater, she was barely recognizable.

The backstage area bustled with other students putting the last-minute touches on their acts, as well. Joel Porter was busy dropping balls in one corner as he practiced his juggling act. Kit spotted Roseanne Parker in a leotard, warming up for her gymnastics act. It didn't fit in with the vaudeville theme, but since she was head cheerleader, she could get away with practically anything. Kit wondered with a pang if Justin was still seeing her, but she soon forgot everything in the general hysteria of the moment.

Lori was peering out at the packed auditorium through a chink in the curtains. "Oh, God, he's sitting in the first row! He's got a bouquiet of roses! I told him I had a boyfriend, and he still hasn't given up."

"Lori, you're absolutely nuts," Elaine told her, laughing. "I wish someone would give *me* roses." She didn't have to say which "someone" she meant. They all knew how she felt about Rusty.

Kit crouched next to Lori to have a peek. She saw her mother sitting in the third row, looking proud and anxious. Things still weren't back to normal between them, even though they tried to act like it. She could tell Janice was still a little hurt about some of the things she'd said. Kit wanted to apologize, but for some reason she hadn't been able to bring herself to do it.

Another familiar face caught her eye, and her heart leaped. Justin was sitting near the back. He was looking straight ahead, his expression calm and serious. Doubts crowded in on her. Maybe the only reason he'd come tonight and covered for her at work was because he felt sorry for her . . .

Lori nudged her. "Do you think we have a chance?" she whispered.

"I hope so," Kit murmured, her gaze still fixed on Justin.

Theirs was one of the first acts to go on, after Adam McArthur's soft-shoe routine. Kit was nervous, but despite Lori's deadly predictions, they sailed through it without a hitch. Kit's voice wobbled a little on the high notes when they sang "By the Light of the Silvery Moon," but no one seemed to notice with Alex belting it out beside her. The audience applauded enthusiastically when they were finished.

Afterwards, Kit rushed to change for her solo act. She barely had enough time to peel off her mustache and wriggle into a pair of tights and her sequined costume before her call was announced.

Hers was a snappy tap routine, danced to the tune of "Puttin' on the Ritz." Alone under the spotlight, Kit forgot about the audience. She forgot about her mother, even about Justin—and lost herself in the pure, wonderful motion of the dance. In a shower of sequinned sparks, she twirled and tapped her way across the stage, never missing a beat. She finished with a dramatic flurry of difficult steps, followed by a show-stopping jump split.

For a fraction of a second the air hung still and time seemed to move in slow motion. Kit was aware of the tiniest things—motes of dust spiraling in the bright cone of the spotlight, the ticking sound of the record player offstage.

Then everything exploded.

The audience went wild. Their applause was a roar in Kit's ears. Someone in the first row stood up. More followed. Suddenly, everyone was standing up. Cheers echoed throughout the auditorium. It was at least five minutes before the noise died down.

Finally, in a state of stunned surprise, Kit managed to find her way offstage. Her friends swooped down on her with shrieks of delight, but Kit was too numb to react. She just stood there, grinning helplessly, while they smothered her in hugs.

"You were the best, the absolute best!" Elaine declared.

Alex caught her in a brisk, bone-crushing embrace. "Poor Roseanne. How can she go on after this?"

Lori thrust a bouquet of roses at Kit. "Here, you deserve these more than I do. Ben will never know the difference." Her blue eyes were misty with happiness for Kit. Kit felt a rush of warmth for her friends. She smiled at the way Alex's mustache had come part way off and was drooping down the side of her chin. Alex was the only person in the world who could make her laugh when she was feeling miserable. And Elaine, true-blue and down-to-earth, was someone she knew she could *always* count on. Then there was Lori, who would put another person's happiness even before her own.

"Do I get a turn?"

Kit whirled around at the sound of the familiar voice. Justin stood near the exit, his hands stuffed in the pockets of his windbreaker. A slow smile spread up from the corners of his mouth to his calm gray eyes.

"You were fantastic," he said.

"So were you," she blurted. "I mean, the way you covered for me with Mr. Watkins. I didn't get a chance to thank you. You practically saved my life."

"It was thanks enough just watching you dance. I wasn't kidding, Kit. You're really good.

125

You could be a professional dancer some day."

Kit blushed. "I'm glad you liked it." She was afraid to move—afraid the magic of this moment might shatter if she so much as breathed.

Then Justin was beside her, touching her shoulder. "Listen, do you want to take a walk? I thought we could talk."

Kit nodded, too overwhelmed with emotion to speak. She forgot that all she had on was her flimsy costume. But Justin hadn't. He took off his windbreaker and slipped it over her shoulders. She shuddered as his warmth spread through her. Without thinking, she reached over and laced her fingers through his.

"You never gave me a chance to explain that night," he said. "What I meant was, I would never hurt you by forcing you to do something you didn't want to do."

They were sitting on a bench in the deserted quad. In the moonlight, Kit watched their shadows blend, forming a single shaft as she moved closer and let her head fall against his shoulder.

"I thought you meant—well, something else," she said, remembering her unreasonable fear and how foolishly quick she'd been to associate Justin's innocent statement with last summer's bad experience. "I guess I wasn't thinking straight."

"Me neither. I should've tried harder to talk to you about it, but I was too mad. I thought you were just trying to get rid of me. Like you changed your mind about us or something."

Kit shook her head. "I thought you'd changed your mind about *me*. Not that I blamed you," she was quick to add. "I mean, who *wouldn't* after the stupid way I acted. Honestly, Justin, I don't know what came over me. I was afraid, I guess."

His eyes widened in surprise. "Of me?"

"Not you exactly. More afraid of myself. Of the way *I* was feeling. It was the first time I ever felt . . . out of control. Did you ever ride a skateboard down a steep hill? Well, that's how it felt. Like—this is fun, but what happens if I fall?"

"The last time I rode a skateboard downhill, I broke two fingers."

"You know what I mean then."

"Yeah, I think I do."

"I wanted to explain everything to you before, but you seemed so distant. I was afraid it was too late."

"I thought you were the one being distant." Justin shook his head. "I guess we were both acting pretty stupid."

She considered telling him about Rich, but decided against it. She just wanted to forget the whole ugly thing. But there was one thing she had to know.

"Are you seeing Roseanne?" she asked. "It's none of my business if you are—I was just wondering."

"What gave you that idea?" Justin asked in surprise.

"I saw you sitting together at lunch, and thought maybe you two were going out together. She's pretty, don't you think?" Kit tried to sound casual, but her voice trembled with emotion.

"Not as pretty as you. Look, Kit, I'm not going out with anyone. In fact, these past couple of weeks have been pretty miserable, if you want to know the truth."

"You mean you're not seeing her?" It took a few seconds for what he'd just said to finally sink in.

"She's in my English class," he explained. "We're doing a project together. That's why I was eating lunch with her."

"Who was that girl at your house then?" Kit blurted.

"What girl?" Justin wanted to know.

Kit told him about the night she'd phoned. She hadn't been planning to—she felt so stupid about hanging up—but she'd panicked.

Justin laughed, shaking his head. "That must have been Cynthia. She's my *father's* girlfriend."

"Oh." Kit was embarrassed. She hadn't even *considered* that possibility.

Kit was quiet for a moment, thinking about the way things had turned out. Then she smiled.

"It's funny, isn't it?" she said. "There you are, thinking your whole life is a total mess, completely hopeless, then an hour later everything is just fine again. I wish I could figure it out."

"If you ever do, let me know."

"But you always seem so sure of yourself," she said.

"Me? That night after the homecoming dance I was so nervous I could hardly see straight. I was as scared as you were about what might happen,

I think."

So it was true, Kit thought. A lot of boys were no different from girls that way. They had just as many insecurities and doubts. The knowledge was comforting, but at the same time a little disconcerting.

"I'm glad you told me," she said.

"Kit, I really care about you." Justin smoothed a wisp of hair from her cheek. "If we ever—well, I wouldn't want it to be like some kind of conquest. We don't have to do it at all if you don't want to."

"Let's just go slow and see, okay?"

He nodded. "Okay."

At the moment, all Kit knew was that she was happier than she'd ever been in her life. She didn't want to think about what was going to happen tomorrow, or the next day. She was content with what she had right now.

They were quiet for a few minutes. Then Kit spoke. "Justin?"

"Mmm."

"I'd like it if you kissed me," she said shyly.

"You would? I wanted to, but I was afraid you would think . . . after what we talked about . . . . oh hell . . ." he stopped talking and kissed her.

Holding him closely, Kit drank in the warmth of his skin, the scent of his fair hair. It felt so good . . . so wonderful to be back in Justin's arms again. Dizzy with joy, she hugged him tighter.

She felt as if she could go on kissing him forever.

Chapter Thirteen

Kit watched her father walk toward her across the crowded restaurant. He looked the same: tall, with broad shoulders that offset the beginning of a paunch, and thinning brown hair. He was wearing his blue suit and a bright green tie she'd given him for his birthday one year. Kit was touched, wondering if he'd worn it on purpose. She jumped up to greet him.

He enveloped her in a crushing bear hug. "Jeez, baby, I'm sorry. The meeting ran late and I couldn't get away. Have you been waiting long?"

Kit had been waiting for about twenty minutes, but she didn't want him to know that. "I just got here," she said.

He grinned. "It's good to see you. You look great! I can hardly believe it. I don't see you for a few months, and look what happens. What did you do with my little Kitten?"

Kit had dressed carefully for this meeting. She had wanted to look as mature as possible and had worn her suede skirt and boots, and a sweater in a heathery shade of blue that matched her eyes. She'd brushed her hair so that it fell in soft waves around her shoulders.

"I guess I grew up, Daddy," she said with more conviction than she felt.

"It's just going to take some getting used to, that's all." He hugged her again before sitting down. "Hey, what do you think of this place? Nice?"

It was an Italian restaurant with lots of dark polished furniture and waiters in white coats who spoke in hushed voices. Kit felt a little intimidated. She felt she could never order what she really wanted in a restaurant like this. She would always look at the menu and think how just one sirloin steak cost as much as she and Janice sometimes spent on groceries for a whole week. It seemed wrong somehow.

"I love it," she said. "But I'm not all that hungry. I think I'll just have soup and salad."

Her father ordered veal marsala and a bottle of wine. He poured her a glass when the waiter wasn't looking. Kit would rather have had milk, but she didn't say so.

"Can't have a proper toast without wine," he said.

"What are we toasting?" Kit's stomach was in knots as she touched her glass to her lips.

"I didn't want to tell you before I was sure, but it

131

looks like the company is transferring me back to this area. I just got the go-ahead on it today. Vi and I are flying up next week to look at houses."

Kit felt a rush of joy, mingled with relief that the news wasn't bad as she'd been anticipating. "That's fantastic, Daddy!"

His brown eyes crinkled up at the corners as he smiled. "I saved the best part for last. Kit, what would you think about coming to live with us? We haven't spent nearly enough time together these past few years, and you'll be going away to college before long. I just thought . . . well, it might be nice. Vi's crazy about the idea, and the girls would love it. What do you say, Kitten?"

Kit didn't know what to think. It was too much all at once. Of course, it would be wonderful to live with her father again, but . . .

"What about Mom?" she asked.

He looked down. "I thought I'd see how you felt about it first. I haven't discussed it with your mother yet."

"It just feels funny somehow, talking about all this without Mom knowing. I think it would upset her."

"Would it?" He was looking at her now, his eyes serious.

That was a good question. Kit thought about it for a minute. *Would* Mom be upset if she moved out? Maybe not. Kit didn't know where she fit into her mother's life anymore. Janice had been spending so much time with Doug these days, Kit rarely saw her.

Of course, Kit reminded herself that she'd been spending a lot of time with Justin, too. In fact, she'd been so absorbed with him these past few weeks she'd hardly been aware of anything else. They spent nearly every evening together. Most of the time, they just met for study dates, but on the weekends they went to the movies or to a party, or they just stayed home and listened to records. She felt so close to him . . . as though she'd known him forever. Justin would understand how torn she felt right now, Kit thought.

"Baby," her father took her hand in his large one, "I only want you to be happy. I'm sure your mother does, too."

"I know, Daddy. I want to, but I'll have to think about it."

"I understand. It's a big decision."

"Can we talk about it with Mom tonight when you take me home?"

"Kit, I don't think now is the—"

"Please? It would help me decide."

"All right, if you say so. I'll do my best." He winked. "But you know how temperamental she can get sometimes."

Kit thought it was a little unfair of him to say that, but she kept her mouth shut. She didn't want to start the kettle boiling before they'd even put the water in.

"I think you're being incredibly selfish about this, Janice." Kit's father spoke in a stern voice, as if she were a child who had gone against his will.

"*I'm* being selfish? What about *you*? You didn't even consider my feelings before you went running to Kit with this crazy scheme of yours."

"That's not the point, and you know it."

"What *is* the point, Frank?"

"The point is we should do what's best for Kit."

Kit wondered why when parents argued about what was best for you, they always acted as if you weren't there. She might as well have been invisible for all they cared at this moment. She sat perched on a chair in the corner of the living room, hugging her knees to her chest and wishing she could really make herself invisible.

Janice stood by the bedroom door in her terry bathrobe. She looked small and defenseless. Her hair was pulled back in a ponytail and she wasn't wearing any makeup. Her face was very red at this moment.

"You think living here with me isn't what's best for Kit?" she demanded, her voice rising.

"I didn't say that. All I said was—"

"It wasn't what you *said*. You never *say* anything. Oh, no, Frank, you're not going to pull that one on me. Don't think I don't know your game after all these years."

"You're getting hysterical," he told her. "All I meant was, it'd be nice for Kit to live in a real home for a change. I wasn't implying you weren't a fit mother."

She shook her head. "You're incredible, you know that? Really incredible. You think you can

134

just waltz in here after three years like—like some kind of Santa Claus, and tell me what Kit and I have isn't a real home. Go to hell, Frank. Just go to hell." She started to cry.

Stop it! Kit wanted to scream. Why didn't they stop? Now she remembered what it had been like before the divorce. Kit had forgotten how bad it was then. Up until now, she'd only let herself remember the good times. Now they were making her remember the way it really was. Tears flooded her eyes. At this moment, she didn't want to live with either one of them. But that was okay, because most likely neither of them wanted her; she was just an excuse for them to fight.

Kit got up, her face wet with tears. Nobody noticed. Nobody cared. They were still fighting when she slipped out the front door.

Chapter Fourteen

Kit didn't realize where she was headed until she was more than halfway there. Justin's house was only a mile or so away, in Glenwood Acres— an area of land where a lot of prefab homes had been built, all looking as if they'd been cut out with cookie cutters. She was two blocks from his house when it started to rain. By the time she got there, she was drenched. *Please be home,* she prayed as she stood on the porch, wet and miserable, waiting for someone to answer the bell.

It was Justin who appeared at the door. He looked as if he'd just taken a shower. His hair stood out in damp ringlets. He was wearing a bulky fisherman's sweater over a pair of faded Levi's.

"Kit!" His gray eyes were lit with surprise. "What are you doing here? You're all wet—I didn't know it was raining. Hey, are you crying?"

Kit stepped into the waiting circle of his arms without saying a word. She buried her face in the warm folds of his sweater while he stroked her dripping hair. He smelled faintly of soap and some kind of piney shampoo. She clung to him for several minutes before she could trust herself to speak.

"Is your father home?" she asked.

"He's working late tonight," Justin told her. "At least that's what he said. I think he's having an affair with one of the secretaries."

"Why would he want to hide it?"

"I don't know. Maybe she's married. Anyway, he's like that. He's not as hip as he wants everyone to think. Under the surface, he's very old-fashioned. Hey, you're shivering. You'd better get out of those wet clothes. I'll give you something of mine to put on."

He found her an old flannel shirt and a pair of jeans that were several sizes too big. She put them on in his room, which, in her opinion, was the nicest room in the house. The walls were a collection of different kinds of posters—one of Bruce Springsteen in concert, another one of a flowering cactus. A brightly woven Indian blanket covered the bed. On a battered desk in the corner was a chessboard and a dog-eared copy of Joseph Conrad's short stories.

After a while, Justin knocked on the door. He came in and sat down next to her on the bed.

"Want to talk about it?"

She told him what had happened between her

parents. "Why do they do that? It's like they don't care about *me*, just about winning."

"I think it's probably both," he said. "They care about you, but they care about winning, too. Nothing like that is ever cut and dried. Anyway, what about you . . . what do *you* want?"

"That's part of the problem. I don't know. Every time I start to think about it I get all tied up inside."

"Are you afraid your mother would be hurt if you moved out—is that it?"

"Partly. Half the time, though, I feel like she doesn't even know I'm there. And the rest of the time—well, we haven't been getting along all that well since she started seeing Doug."

Justin leaned back against the headboard, a rueful smile on his lips. "I know what you mean about that. Dad's been serious with about five women since my parents split up. With the first one, I was still too much in shock to know what was going on, but by the third I guess I was ready for him to get married again. I really liked Patty. She knew how to do a lot of neat stuff—like deep-sea fishing and hang-gliding—that kind of thing."

"She sounds like Alex."

"Yeah. Only that wasn't all. She was smart about a lot of things. She was the one who told me that people should only get married if they're happy spending time alone, too. That way, they don't depend on the other person so much. But I guess she liked being by herself a little too

138

much."

"I felt that way about Hugh, my mother's first boyfriend," Kit confided.

"What it boils down to is, you've got to accept the fact that our parents are just as messed up about things like that as kids our age. I guess love is as hard to find when you're forty as it is when you're seventeen."

Kit was looking at Justin in a way she'd never looked at him before. She realized that she was seeing him as a whole person, not just as a boy she liked. Someone she could share her thoughts and worries with the same way she did with her friends. How she felt about him went much deeper than hand-holding and kissing.

She'd always thought of love as some big romantic thing where a couple went around staring into each other's eyes and complimenting one another. She'd never thought of it like this, as something comfortable and easy.

Did she love Justin? Yes, she supposed she did. It was funny, she thought, because up until now she'd always imagined love in capital letters—something that hit you over the head instead of sneaking up on you quietly.

Suddenly, she was acutely aware of Justin's gaze on her. She was sure he must know what she was thinking.

"I like your room," she said, looking around. "Especially that poster over there, the one of the cactus."

"I got it in Arizona when I was visiting my mom

last summer. She was filming an archeological dig."

"It reminds me of you."

"What—the cactus?"

"No, silly, the room."

He laughed. "You mean because it's not modern like the rest of the house? You should've heard the fight Dad and I had over it. He wanted to throw out everything and buy all new stuff. But I happen to like it this way. You don't have to worry about everything getting beat-up because it already is."

Kit smiled. "I didn't mean I liked it because it was beat-up."

"I know." He took her hand, lightly pressing each one of her knuckles with his thumb.

Kit felt a slow warmth spread through her. Justin understood so much. Right now, for instance, he knew, without either of them having to say it, that she wanted him to kiss her.

They lay on the bed kissing for a long time. Justin was the first to draw away. He was trembling, his eyes a dark, smoky gray. Kit blinked. Gradually, she became aware that both of them were breathing too fast and that the air in the room was close and hot. She waited for the "wrong" buzzer to go off in her brain the way it always did, but nothing happened. Somehow, being with Justin this way didn't seem wrong.

"We'd better stop," he said in a shaky voice.

"Why?" Kit touched his hair.

"Because if we don't, I'm not going to want to in

a few seconds."

"That's okay. I don't want you to stop." The words were out before she even realized she'd said them.

Justin didn't do anything at first. He just held her, stroking the back of her neck. She could feel his heart beating wildly. She listened to the rain being flung against the window, the far-off thump of a garage door slamming shut.

"Are you sure?" he asked. Kit nodded against his shoulder.

They took their clothes off, then lay side by side kissing for a while. Kit wasn't sure if she should have her eyes open or shut. She decided to keep them open to look at Justin. She thought he was beautiful—if it was okay for a boy to be beautiful. Smoothing her hand over his back, Kit felt his muscles tighten at her touch. He shifted so that he was on top of her.

"Okay?" he murmured. "Am I hurting you?"

"A little," she said. "You elbow was pinching me, that's all. It's okay now."

She smiled. He looked so worried, his face all furrowed. She kissed him deeply. A warm current of tenderness rushed through her.

"Kit," he whispered, stroking her hair. His hand was trembling.

She could feel the rapid beating of his heart. It felt as if it were inside her own chest. Then she realized it was—her own heart was beating just as quickly. She thought about what Janice had said, about sex being as natural as breathing.

Maybe so but, of the two, sex was a lot more interesting, she decided.

Afterward, in the darkness, Justin rested his hand against her cheek. "I love you," he said.

"You don't have to," she told him.

"I know. I really do, though. It's not just because we made love."

She curled up against him. "I feel the same way. That was . . ." she searched for the right description, but couldn't find it.

"Yeah, I know."

She laughed softly. "How come you always know what I'm thinking?"

"Because I'm thinking it, too."

"Justin?"

"What?"

"Have you ever been in love before?"

"No."

"It's nicer this way, don't you think? Both of us in love for the first time, and everything feeling so right.

"Mmm." He kissed her. "Know what I'm thinking now?"

She grinned. "I can guess." Reluctantly, she untangled herself from his arms. "I'd better go. I wish I didn't have to, but I have a feeling I should. My mom is probably wondering where I disappeared to."

She got up and began putting her clothes on, thinking how nice it was that she could get dressed in front of a boy and not be self-conscious about it. With Justin, everything felt natural.

Kit was struggling into her jeans, which were still damp from the rain, when suddenly her feelings for Justin and what had just happened between them overwhelmed her. Her legs started trembling so badly she had to sit down on the bed. She felt both sad and unbearably happy.

Justin held her while she cried.

Kit found her mother curled up asleep on the couch when she got home. She looked so defenseless, Kit felt a wave of sympathy wash over her. She was sorry for the way she'd blamed her mother for everything that was wrong with her life. Nothing was easy for Janice, either. Maybe she was looking for the kind of love Kit had found with Justin. That kind of love wasn't easy to find.

Kit touched her shoulder. "Mom?"

Janice blinked, then sat up. "What time is it?" she asked groggily.

"It's after midnight. I hope you weren't worried. I was at Justin's."

"Kit . . ." Janice held out her arms. She hugged Kit tightly. "I'm just glad you're back. Oh, honey, I *was* worried, but not the way you think. I was afraid—well, after what your father said, I was afraid you . . . you felt the way he did. That this wasn't a real home."

"Dad was just mad when he said that. He didn't mean it. Anyway, it's not true."

A sad little smile touched her lips. "I know I'm not always the best mother. And sometimes do the wrong thing. But I want you to know I do love you."

"I know, Mom." Kit felt a rush of warmth for her mother. "I love you, too."

It was true. Theirs might not be the traditional mother-daughter relationship—Janice had never sewn her a dress or contributed a cake for a PTA bake sale—but she was fun to be with and that counted for a lot, didn't it? Kit remembered the time she'd arrived home from school to find a pile of wrapped presents on her bed. "Happy Unbirthday," her mother had written on the cards. That was just the kind of thing Janice would do . . . always when you least expected it. Crazy, unpredictable little surprises like trips to the zoo on a school day, chocolate eclairs for Sunday breakfast, and once, a kitten—even though Janice was allergic to cats.

"I'm sorry about the way I blew up tonight," Janice said. "It's just that he makes me so mad sometimes." She took a deep breath. "Kit, I want you here with me, but I won't stand in your way if you'd rather be with your father. I just want you to be happy."

"I *am* happy." The truth was, at this moment, she'd never been happier in her whole life. "Sometimes I think *you'd* be happier without me around all the time, though. I mean, you and Doug . . . well, you'd have more freedom."

Janice's eyes filled with tears as she shook her head slowly. "Is that how it seems to you? Oh, Kit, you couldn't be more wrong. If I didn't have you—" her voice broke. Finally, with a weak little

144

laugh, she said, "Anyhow, who else would be crazy enough to laugh at my jokes?"

"We're a team, remember? And good comedy acts are hard to find these days."

They were both laughing and crying at the same time as they hugged each other.

"You know what?" Janice sniffed a few minutes later. "I'm hungry."

Kit realized she was starved, too. All she'd had to eat tonight was a bowl of soup. "What's in the refrigerator?"

"Nothing. I threw out all the leftovers this morning. They looked suspiciously moldy. Anyway, I'm in the mood for Chinese."

"Mom! It's after midnight. There's nothing open that late around here."

"San Francisco is only forty minutes away. I know of a great little all-night place in Chinatown," she suggested hopefully.

Kit looked at her mother like she was crazy, then she grinned. "I'll get my jacket."

Chapter Fifteen

Kit squeezed in next to Lori in the backseat of Alex's car. "Are you sure we can make it to school in this? It sounds terminally ill."

"Don't worry." Alex gave the steering wheel an affectionate pat. "All it needs is a new muffler. We could probably make it to New York City in this thing."

"Some other time," Elaine said. "I have a Chemistry quiz this morning. If I miss it, I'm dead."

"You're always saying that," Lori giggled. "And you're the one who'll end up at Stanford while the rest of us are plugging away in community college."

Elaine gave a sly smile, her brown eyes twinkling. "That's because I'm smarter than the rest of you—*I* know that the ratio of boys to girls at Stanford is three to one. Why else do you think I want to get in?"

"Speaking of the opposite sex, how's it going with Rusty?" Alex wanted to know.

Elaine shrugged. "Same thing. The Invisible Woman Meets the Incredible Hunk. I start tutoring him next week. Maybe he'll fall in love with my mind and we can work our way down from there."

"Hmm, maybe we can help you come up with a game plan for the first session," Alex said. She turned to Kit. "Have any ideas, Kit?"

"Mmm," Kit murmured, staring out the window. Only half of her attention was on the conversation.

It was strange how she felt. Like she wasn't altogether here, riding to school with her friends; she was in a dream, a dream about Justin. She could still feel the warm imprint of his body and the image of his face every time she closed her eyes. Yet at the same time, everything around her was incredibly focused. Colors had never seemed brighter or smells sharper. She saw beauty in ordinary everyday things. The laundry flapping on Mrs. Lanitsky's clothesline became a prize-winning photograph in her mind. *She* was the same, but overnight the world had changed.

"Hey, is anyone home?" Someone was waving a hand in front of her face. Lori.

"Huh?" Kit looked around. "Sorry. Guess I was daydreaming."

"You've been in a trance since you got in the car," Elaine observed. "What gives?"

Kit felt her face go warm and prickly. Should

she tell them? Would they understand? In the past, she'd always confided everything to them, but this was different. This was private and special . . .

She should have remembered, though, that it was nearly impossible to hide anything from Elaine.

Elaine was leaning over the front seat, peering at her. She spoke in a hushed, reverential voice. "Something happened between you and Justin last night, didn't it? I can just tell. You look different. *Did* something happen?"

Kit nodded, unable to speak.

Lori clapped a hand over her mouth. "You don't mean—you really—oh, Kit, I don't believe it!"

Alex took a more practical approach. "What was it like?"

"Nice," Kit said.

"That's all . . . no fireworks . . . no bells going off . . . just *nice*?" Lori looked a little disappointed.

"You've been watching too many movies," Alex told her. To Kit, she said, "I hope it's nice when it happens with Danny and me."

"Do you feel any different?" Elaine asked.

Kit smiled. "Sort of. Mostly I just feel . . . well, I'm not sorry about it, if that's what you mean. And I'm glad it happened with Justin. With anyone else, it would have been pretty empty, I think." She was silent for a moment. Then she said, "It's like when you're listening to music and you're not just *hearing* it, but you also start to

148

wonder what kind of mood the composer was in when he wrote it—whether he was happy or really miserable about something in his life—and then after a while you feel whatever he was feeling too. I guess I'm trying to say that making love should be that way—caring about each other's feelings instead of just doing it."

"It's so romantic," Lori sighed. "When it happens to me, I want to hear Beethoven's Ninth."

"I'll settle for something a little simpler," Alex said. "That way I won't be disappointed." She laughed. "I remember when I thought how crazy it was, the idea of my parents ever doing it. Well, I wonder what they were thinking when they conceived me."

"They were probably thinking about the Olympics," Lori giggled.

"Mine were thinking about having a boy," Elaine said. "My mother told me they had a name all picked out and everything, even before she found out she was pregnant. Just think, one little Y chromosome and my name would have been Stanley Marshall Gregory."

"Stanley?" Kit started to laugh. Somehow, she couldn't picture Elaine as a Stanley.

Alex turned into the school parking lot, and Kit felt herself tense up. This was where the dream ended and reality began. What would it be like when she saw Justin at school? Would he act as if nothing had happened? Would he be sorry today he'd told her he loved her?

By the time Kit got to her first class, she was so

nervous she could hardly stand it.

In Drama, which Kit had third period, they were doing a scene from *A Streetcar Named Desire*. Kit was playing the part of Blanche, the crazy sister. She'd rehearsed the scene with Jeff Beck, but he was absent that day, so Mr. Whitson chose Derek Johnson. Derek wasn't too happy about it.

"Who *is* this Stanley Kowalski creep, anyway?" he wanted to know after scanning a few lines.

"Oh, you shouldn't have any trouble with the part," Marcia Connors said sweetly. "He's a macho pig just like you."

Marcia was playing the part of his wife, Stella. Kit had heard somewhere that Marcia and Derek had broken up. The reason was now obvious. She warmed to Marcia for the first time. Maybe there was hope for her yet.

The scene was a huge success, mostly because of the way Derek grunted and growled his way through his lines. Kit was in another world, thinking about Justin, so she made a perfect, dreamy-eyed Blanche. Mr. Whitson gave each of them an A, except Marcia, who got a B+.

"Stella's supposed to be in love with Stanley; she doesn't want to scratch his eyes eyes out. I think you're injecting too much of your own feelings into the part," he observed shrewdly.

Everyone in the class laughed, except Derek. After the bell, he came up to Kit.

"Not bad," he said.

"You were pretty good yourself," she told him.

He shrugged. "Hey, I heard you were going with Kennerly. That true?"

Was it? Kit's heart was pounding so loudly she was sure it could be heard over the shuffling of feet and slamming of books. Last night seemed like a hundred years ago. Was it possible Justin could still feel the same about her today?

"I'm late," she said, quickly gathering up her books.

Derek followed her out the door. Suddenly, Kit remembered something she'd heard once—that a boy could tell if a girl is a virgin by the way she walks. Derek was just the type to notice something like that. Kit wondered if she was walking any differently. Just in case, she tried holding herself very straight and taking smaller steps.

"Something wrong?" Derek asked.

"What?" Kit's cheeks were burning as she turned to face him.

"You were walking kind of funny. I thought maybe you stepped on something."

"Uh . . . no. Look, I've gotta run. I'm really late." She hurried ahead, feeling as if her face were on fire.

She didn't even notice Justin until she'd practically bumped into him. She froze in the middle of the busy corridor, staring at him as if he were the last person on earth she expected to see. He was wearing tan cords and a light purple polo shirt. Kit took a deep breath. She felt as if she were made of glass and the wrong word, the tini-

151

est wrong glance would shatter her.

"Hi," he said. His gaze lingered on her. "I was looking for you."

"You were?" Kit's voice emerged as a squeak. "Anything special?"

"Not really. I just wanted to see you."

"You did?"

"Kit . . . what's the matter? You're acting sort of funny. Is anything wrong?"

"N-no," she stammered. "Well, actually, the truth is . . . I *feel* a little funny." She dropped her voice to a whisper. "You know what I mean?"

He nodded thoughtfully. "Yeah, I think so. But it's a *nice* funny. Kit, you're not sorry, are you?"

"Are you?"

He smiled as he shook his head.

"I'm not either," she said. "I was just afraid."

"Afraid of what?"

"Of . . . I don't know . . . everything. I was afraid you didn't really mean all those things you said last night."

"Oh, Kit." He put his arms around her—there, right in the middle of the hallway, with everyone looking.

"I love *you*, not just your body," he murmured against her ear, holding her so tightly she could hardly breathe.

After a minute or so, he said, "Come on. I'll walk you to class."

"It's all the way up in the Science building. You'll be late for yours."

He shrugged. "I don't mind."

Kit's heart was soaring. She danced up on tip-toe and kissed his cheek. "You're crazy."

"That's why you love me, right?"

"Right. Among other reasons."

"Yeah, like what?"

"Oh, the list is too long. It'd take me forever to name them all."

"Good thing I'm the patient type."

He kept his arm around her as they walked up the hill. Kit didn't speak; her happiness was too great. Looking up at Justin, she saw that it wasn't necessary to try and explain how she felt.

He already understood.

2. SMART ENOUGH TO KNOW

Only Elaine Gregory's closest friends, Kit, Alex, and Lori, know that she's also the rowdy school mascot, Wilbur the Wildcat. To the rest of the school, she is shy, soft-spoken Elaine The Brain.

So when she's asked to tutor handsome Rusty, Elaine is excited but terrified. Flirting with the popular football player is easy when she's dressed as Wilbur, but will Rusty ever see anything romantic in plain old Elaine? To make matters worse, there's trouble at home. Even Elaine can't figure out what to do—although everyone thinks she's *Smart Enough to Know.*

3. WINNER ALL THE WAY

For lean, tawny Alex Enomoto, competitive sports are a way of life. Nobody understands this better than Alex's boyfriend, Danny, also a dedicated athlete. What Danny doesn't understand is Alex's need to succeed twice—once for herself, and once for her brother, who's seriously ill.

Alex's competitiveness approaches obsession when she finds out that an Olympic coach will be at her next diving meet. Alex's three best friends, Kit, Elaine, and Lori, grow concerned about her single-minded pursuit. But Alex refuses to listen to them. She is determined to get what she wants—even at the expense of Danny's love. She doesn't realize how hard it is to be a *Winner All The Way.*

4. AFRAID TO LOVE

Tall and slender, with long blond hair and a perfect smile, Lori Woodhouse is a beauty by everyone's definition—except her own. In her mind, she's still the overweight girl she used to be before she moved to Glenwood a year ago. But nobody knows about the old Lori. Not even Kit, Alex, or elaine, her best friends. Even worse, they don't realize that Lori is hiding an alcoholic father.

But Lori's plan to keep her past a secret threatens to backfire when Perry, a boy from her old school, moves into the area. Lori's determined to keep him out of her life, but the harder she tries to avoid him, the more he chases after her. Will Perry find out who Lori really is? Will he discover why she is *Afraid to Love*?